HEDGEROWS AND VERGES

TITLES OF RELATED INTEREST

Biogeographical processes
I. G. Simmons

Class experiments in plant physiology
H. Meidner

Comparative plant ecology
J. P. Grime *et al.*

Countryside conservation
B. Green

Energy flow in ecosystems
P. Wells & M. Watson

Estimating the size of animal populations
J. H. Blower *et al.*

Freshwater studies
J. H. R. Gee

Grassland studies
J. Brodie

Historical plant geography
P. Stott

*Insects and flowers**
F. G. Barth

Introduction to vegetation analysis
D. R. Causton

Introduction to world vegetation
A. S. Collinson

Landscape meanings and values
E. C. Penning-Rowsell & D. Lowenthal (eds)

Light and plant growth
J. W. Hart

National parks
A. & M. MacEwen

Nature's place
W. M. Adams

Patterns of life
H. Mielke

Plant breeding systems
A. J. Richards

Plants for arid lands
G. E. Wickens *et al.* (eds)

Saltmarsh and estuary studies
M. Jenkins

Seashore studies
M. Jenkins

Upland and moorland studies
D. F. Quorroll & D. M. Hall

Urban ecology
D. Smith

* Not available from Allen & Unwin in North America

HEDGEROWS AND VERGES

W. H. DOWDESWELL

London
ALLEN & UNWIN
Boston   Sydney

Allen & Unwin (Publishers) Ltd,
40 Museum Street, London WC1A 1LU, UK

Allen & Unwin (Publishers) Ltd,
Park Lane, Hemel Hempstead, Herts HP2 4TE, UK

Allen & Unwin, Inc.,
8 Winchester Place, Winchester, Mass. 01890, USA

Allen & Unwin, (Australia) Ltd,
8 Napier Street, North Sydney, NSW 2060, Australia

First published in 1987

British Library Cataloguing in Publication Data

Dowdeswell, W.H.
  Hedgerows and verges.
1. Windbreaks, shelterbelts, etc.—
Great Britain
I. Title
574.5′2643   SD409.5
ISBN 0–04–574040–2
ISBN 0–04–574041–0 Pbk

Library of Congress Cataloging in Publication Data

Dowdeswell, W.H. (Wilfrid Hogarth)
  Hedgerows and verges.
Bibliography: p.
Includes index.
1. Hedgerow ecology – England. 2. Roadside ecology –
England. 3. Windbreaks, shelterbelts, etc. – England. 4. Roads
– England – Shoulders. I. Title.
QH138.A1D68 1986   574.5′264   86–17256
ISBN 0–04–0574040–2
ISBN 0–04–574041–0 (pbk.)

Set in 10 on 11 point Concorde by Phoenix Photosetting, Chatham
and printed in Great Britain by St Edmundsbury Press, Suffolk

Preface

Patterns of intersecting hedgerows constitute one of the predominant features of our landscape. Many hedges are of great antiquity, being remnants of woodland that existed in Norman times, and before. But the majority were planted from the medieval period onwards and originally formed the boundaries of property, later becoming integrated into the changing patterns of agriculture and providing fences, shelter and windbreaks. Banks and hedges often form the boundaries of roads and tracks, many of which are of ancient origin. Their age can sometimes be determined from documents and, within certain limits, by the nature and diversity of the plant species inhabiting them.

Verges are of more recent origin and their structure and ecology are of particular interest since they reflect, often with great sensitivity, the influence of human management on the environment in which they are situated.

Besides their historical and social interest, hedgerows and verges are of increasing significance as rich reservoirs of plant and animal life. As long as an appreciable proportion of the adjacent land remained largely undisturbed, the composition of these communities often mirrored that of the surrounding fields and woodland. But with the advent of intensive agriculture, much of the former field wildlife has been destroyed, and hedgerows and verges have become the last bastion against its final extermination. Of recent years, the policy of grubbing up hedges to facilitate the use of ever larger agricultural machinery has further aggravated the situation.

In spite of their ubiquity and comparative ease of access, hedgerows and verges fail to attract the attention and interest they deserve. The purpose of this book is to provide a stimulating and up-to-date account of these environments, and problems associated with them. It is written from the point of view of anyone wishing to find out more about this fascinating and much disregarded part of our landscape. Since both hedgerows and verges are man-made, their management and survival pose peculiar problems that are not found elsewhere and provide a realistic insight into the process of conservation in both its ecological and human aspects.

vii

Since the text makes only modest demands on previous knowledge, it should be suitable for a wide range of backgrounds and interests. Technical terms have been kept to a minimum and, when unavoidable, they have been explained as they arise and also summarised in the glossary. At the end of the book will also be found a list of references, a bibliography and a selection of organisations concerned in various ways with hedgerows and verges from whom further information can be obtained.

My sincere thanks are due to David Streeter for kindly reading the typescript and for numerous helpful comments and suggestions, which have been of the greatest value, and also to Mr John Hooper for providing me with unpublished research information on hedgerow environments.

It is a pleasure to thank Sue Fairhurst for drawing some of the figures, and Elaine Cromwell and Beryl Roberts for the patience and efficiency with which they have prepared the several drafts of the typescript, and the index. I would also like to take this opportunity of thanking all those who have permitted me to reproduce data, tables and diagrams from their published work, detailed acknowledgement of which is made elsewhere.

W. H. Dowdeswell
Atworth, Melksham

Acknowledgements

The author would like to thank the following people, institutions and publishers for permission to reproduce material in this work (numbers in parentheses refer to text figures unless otherwise stated):

The University of Cambridge Committee for Aerial Photography (1.1b, 8.1 – Cambridge University Collection: copyright reserved); the Royal Commission on the Historical Monuments of England (1.2, 1.3 – National Monuments Record Air Photograph. Crown Copyright Reserved); T. Rowley and J. Wood (1.4); Avon County Council (1.13); Collins (6.7 and Table 2.1); the Natural Environment Research Council (Table 2.2); the British Association for Local History (2.4, 2.5); the Nature Conservancy Council (2.8, 7.6); the editor of the *Journal of Ecology* (2.9); Eric and David Hosking (4.1, 4.2, 4.4); the editor of the *Journal of Applied Ecology* (4.3, 4.6); S. Beaufoy (4.7, 6.5); the editor of *Environmental Pollution* (5.2); N. Scott and A. Davison (5.3); F. Sturrock, J. Cathie and the University of Cambridge Department of Land Economy (6.2, 6.3, 8.2 and Tables 6.1 & 6.3); the editor of *The Ecologist* (Table 6.2); the Agricultural Training Board (7.5); the Countryside Commission (8.3); and Wessex Newspapers (8.5).

Contents

List of tables

1

The origins of hedgerows and verges

What is a hedgerow? To anyone who is at all familiar with the countryside, the answer is self-evident. It is a narrow belt of vegetation, dominated by a variety of shrubs and occasional trees, separating one area of land from another. The characteristic patterns formed by the intersection of hedges provide the backcloth to much of our existing landscape (Fig. 1.1). But only a short journey from one part of the country to another will soon reveal appreciable differences in appearance, showing that such a generalised definition is of only limited value.

Hedgerows are essentially man-made structures. Their character depends upon their mode of origin and subsequent maintenance, upon the uses they serve and upon a variety of ecological factors, such as the climate and the nature of the soil. So if we wish to gain a deeper understanding of their history, ecology and significance, it will be necessary to trace them back to their origins and follow their history insofar as we can. Adaptation is a process involving responses to a continuously changing environment. In what contexts did hedgerows arise and become adapted to the diverse requirements of man? What forces have been responsible for the situation that we find today?

Barriers and boundaries

One approach to a study of the historical roles of hedges is to seek to discover at the outset the origin of the word 'hedge'. A precise answer is not easy to obtain. One of the principal problems is that, even as late as the mid-19th century, the names of persons, places and things were communicated largely by word of mouth and seldom written down. As a consequence, the origins of words, their uses and particularly their spellings were

1

Figure 1.1 Intersecting hedges with trees provide the backcloth to much of our landscape: (a) Devonshire and (b) Cheshire.

subject to surprising variations. In 18th-century documents, for instance, it is not at all uncommon to find the name of some well known locality spelt in three different ways on the same page! There is little doubt that the word 'hedge' is of Anglo-Saxon origin, and I am grateful to David Streeter for pointing out that its derivation is more complicated than is sometimes supposed. It seems that three words have given rise to our modern usage: *haeg*, meaning hurdle; *hecg*, referring to a territorial boundary either dead or planted; and *hega*, a living or border boundary. *Hecg* has given rise to our modern 'hedge'; *hega* is the origin of the modern 'haw', as in hawthorn; while *haeg* is the basis for 'hay', as in numerous place names such as Hayling. Incidentally, it is worth noting that the Saxon *hēg*, also meaning 'hay' (dead grass), is of quite a different origin and has no connection with any hedge names.

It is sometimes said that the word 'hedgerow' referred at one time to two hedges with a track running between them, but that is a usage which does not apply today. There now seems to be no good reason for distinguishing between hedge and hedgerow, which can be regarded as synonymous and are used as alternatives throughout this book.

Traditionally, the hedge has served two purposes: as a barrier to the movement of livestock, and as a means of marking out the boundaries of property. From prehistoric times until the end of the Saxon period (late 9th century), farmers were faced with the additional problem of protecting their livestock against wild animals, particularly wolves. It is significant that the castle at Winchester where King Alfred established himself and assembled the *Anglo-Saxon Chronicle* in the late 9th century was called Wolvesey (meaning 'island of wolves'), a name retained today for the palace of the Bishop of Winchester, which is built on the same site.

The Iron Age (*c.* 550–50 BC) was characterised by the construction of protective fortifications such as Maiden Castle in Dorset, which provides an outstanding example (Fig. 1.2). It is of particular interest since, unlike most of these encampments, it was later captured and occupied by the Romans, as is shown by the presence of a small temple on the site. The ditches were surmounted by wooden stockades, evidence of this being the uncovering of some of the larger post holes during recent excavations. Many of these forts, particularly those sited on hilltops, must have had important military value; others were constructed in comparatively low-lying and accessible localities where their main purpose was probably the everyday protection of people

Figure 1.2 Maiden Castle, Dorset, an outstanding example of an Iron Age fortification later occupied by the Romans.

and livestock from wild animals. This might also have been the function of the many ancient pounds that have been discovered, such as Grimspound on Dartmoor (Fig. 1.3), a formidable enclosure about 300 m (275 yards) across with a base of large rocks into which domestic animals were no doubt herded by night. Used in this context, the word 'pound' has survived to this day as an enclosure for accommodating stray livestock.

4

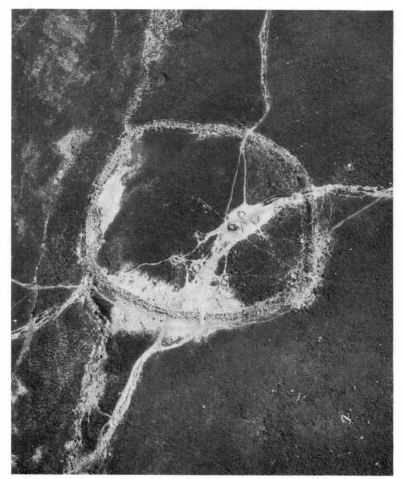

Figure 1.3 Grimspound on Dartmoor (Devon), a formidable Bronze Age enclosure.

The people of the Bronze Age used a type of plough (the ard) that was drawn by oxen and did not turn over the soil like a modern plough but made a wide furrow. Ploughing was done both along and across in order to break up the soil thoroughly, and so led to the formation of fields of convenient size – the so-called 'Celtic' fields of 0.2–0.8 hectares (ha) (0.5–2 acres). These persisted throughout the Iron Age that followed and continued into the Roman period. **Lynchets** (low banks) marked the outlines of the fields, and these denoted boundaries but were not cattle barriers.

The Saxons were village dwellers and cultivated groups of fields with an area of waste ground between them, which was gradually used up as the population expanded. The fields were ploughed in strips that were grouped together into **furlongs**, providing the basic units for crop rotation. The size of each furlong varied somewhat depending on local conditions. The standard unit was 1 acre (0.4 ha), 1 furlong in length (220 yards = 200 m) and 4 rods wide (22 yards = 20 m), but smaller areas were quite common. The strips were each ploughed separately and were often separated from one another by grassy banks (**balks**). This pattern of **strip cultivation** continued into medieval times and is beautifully illustrated in the village of Lower Heyford, Oxfordshire (Fig. 1.4). Elsewhere, some strips survive to this day and are still in cultivation, as can be seen on Portland, Dorset (Fig. 1.5). Later ploughing frequently eliminated the former strips but left the balks standing above ground level – a condition referred to as **ridge and furrow**. It is particularly evident where former arable land has been converted to pasture.

Figure 1.4 Plan of the strip field system at Lower Heyford, Oxfordshire, in 1604.[68]

6

Figure 1.5 Medieval strip cultivation on Portland, Dorset, still in use. The ridge-and-furrow pattern is clearly visible.

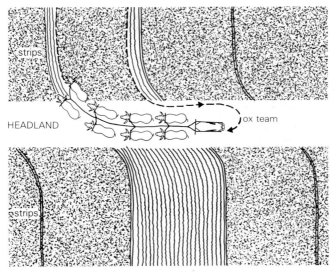

strips

HEADLAND

ox team

strips

Figure 1.6 The origin of S-shaped field contours. By adopting a curved approach when ploughing, the turning distance of an ox team could be reduced by as much as half.

A feature of many medieval strip systems was that, instead of terminating in a straight line, they and their lynchets sometimes ended in a curve, the whole strip thus approximating to the shape of an elongated S. Ploughing was frequently by teams of eight oxen yolked together in pairs, and approaching the end of a furrow in a straight line would have necessitated a turning distance (headland) of around 10 m (11 yards). By adopting a curved approach as in Figure 1.6, the turning distance could be reduced by as much as half and a considerable saving in ground therefore achieved. With the rise of sheep farming in the 16th century, many of these ancient field systems began to fall into disuse and no doubt became colonised by trees and shrubs, which eventually formed hedges preserving the familiar S-shape (see p. 7). Since little new strip cultivation began after about 1400, the S-like contours of an existing hedge provide a useful means of establishing its latest date of origin. This can often be confirmed from the outlines of former furrows and lynchets nearby, which are visible from aerial photographs or on the ground when it is covered in snow.

The Saxon hedge

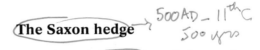

In Saxon times from approximately 500 AD until the coming of the Normans in the 11th century, much of the country (probably as much as 70 per cent in places) was still wooded. Particularly in Southern England and the Midlands, many human settlements were in woodland clearings. By modern standards, fields were small and the numbers of livestock few. The requirement, therefore, was for easily erected barriers ('dead hedges') to prevent animals from straying, which could quickly be moved to other sites as grazing became exhausted. Wood was plentiful and the early hedges were probably lightweight structures resembling the chestnut palings used for the temporary herding of sheep today (Fig. 1.7). Although we have no direct evidence of this, occasionally tradition comes to our aid, providing us with an important link with the past in the form of local ceremonies and customs that have survived the years. One of these occurs in Yorkshire in the form of the Whitby Penny (a corruption of 'penance')[1]. In 1159, three knights and their pack of hounds were hunting a wounded boar, which went to ground in a hermitage occupied by a monk of Whitby Abbey. While attempting to save the boar, the monk was set upon by the hounds and inadvertently killed. The three knights escaped due punishment only

Figure 1.7 Movable palings of the kind probably used for early field boundaries.

because the dying monk forgave them. Whereupon, the Abbot ordained that, each year on the Eve of Ascension, their successors should construct a length of paling on the seashore according to his specification such that it 'stand three tides without removing by the force of the water'. Failure to comply with these commands would mean the forfeiting of their lands to the Abbot. The **Penny Hedge** constructed annually at Whitby may well bear a fairly close resemblance to the kind of structure that surrounded the fields of the 12th century, illustrated in Figure 1.7 and still existing today. Wilson[2] quotes what may well be one of the earliest statements on the function of a hedge in the laws of the Saxon King Ine dated 688 and 694, which required that owners of livestock be responsible for stopping their cattle from attacking other farmers' crops. The 'fence' around a property was required to be stockproof.

Dead hedges today

Today, in many parts of the country, the functions of hedges are still performed by dead structures. Some of the most characteristic are the stone walls typical of Wiltshire, the Cotswolds and many areas in the North (Fig. 1.8). These not only serve as boundaries to property and barriers to animal movement, but in exposed areas they also provide valuable windbreaks and shelter for sheep. In Cornwall, where much of the country is exposed to the full force of the wind and rain, and the rate of erosion is therefore high, field barriers tend to assume the form of earth banks faced with stones or stones sealed together by earth. Such structures are known collectively as 'hedges' and their construction is

9

Figure 1.8 Dry stone walls typical of Wiltshire, the Cotswolds and many areas in the North.

an ancient art that has accumulated over the years a picturesque vernacular.[3] In order to minimise the effects of erosion and to prevent bulging (**bellying**), the sides of the hedge are set at a slope (**batter**) inclining inwards towards the top (Fig. 1.9a). To ensure uniformity of construction and a correct batter, an iron frame (**pattern**) is sometimes used as a guide (Fig. 1.9b). Occasionally, a new hedge is planted with small shrubs and herbs, but more often colonisation is a natural process, as in Figure 1.10 and 1.11.

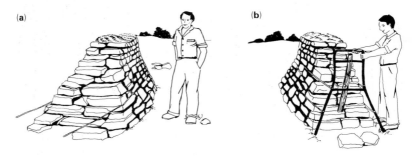

Figure 1.9 Constructing a Cornish hedge: (a) to minimise the effects of erosion, the sides are set at a slope (batter); (b) to ensure uniformity, an iron frame (pattern) is sometimes used.

10

Figure 1.10   Colonisation of a wall by shrubs, Tregunnon, Cornwall.

Figure 1.11   Colonisation of a wall by heather, Exmoor, Somerset.

As late as the 18th century, large individual stones (**meare-stones**) were also often used as a means of identifying the boundaries of property, some of which became incorporated in hedges planted later. An example is the Edgerley Stone (Fig. 1.12), which lies in the north bank of the road from Simonsbath to Challa-

11

Figure 1.12 The Edgerley Stone, a large 18th-century mearestone in the north bank of the Simonsbath to Challacombe road (B3358), which still marks the boundary between Somerset and Devon.

combe (B3358) and still marks the county boundary between Somerset and Devon. Nearby, the Sloley Stone, erected in 1742, bears no relationship to any modern boundary but goes a step further by recording the names of former neighbouring landowners: on one side 'William Longe Oxenham Esquire Lord of the Manor of Highbray 1742', and on the other 'Christian Slowley Lady of the Manor of Gratton'.

The origins of living hedges

As we have seen (p. 12) the name of one of our commonest hedgerow plants, the hawthorn, has an Anglo-Saxon origin. But precisely when the first hedges were planted is uncertain. From the early documents, one thing is clear. The replacement of dead structures by living ones was a gradual process and proceeded at varying rates in different parts of the country. Several features combined to bring these changes about. One was probably economic: it was considered cheaper to plant a boundary as a permanency than to construct, maintain and move about sections of palings. This argument became increasingly valid as the area of individual fields became larger. In the 12th century it was customary for landowners to clear areas of woodland for farming purposes (assarts) and lease them to tenants as a source of income. The boundaries of these assarts will have been composed of trees and shrubs, and the early hedges may well have been derived from communities of plant species already in existence at the forest edge. There is evidence from their composition that some of these ancient hedges still survive today. Thus Pollard[4] has shown in the Huntingdon and Peterborough areas that certain plant species are poor colonisers of planted hedgerows, being found mainly in those derived from former woodland. These include trees and shrubs such as oak (*Quercus* spp.), field maple (*Acer campestre*), hazel (*Corylus avellana*), spindle (*Euonymus europaeus*) and dogwood (*Cornus sanguinea*). Certain herbs, when present, are also probably relics of woodland or wood edge vegetation, such as dog's mercury (*Mercurialis perennis*), bluebell (*Endymion non-scriptus*) and primrose (*Primula vulgaris*). One reason for the apparently clearcut distinction in these areas between woodland and non-woodland hedges could be that the fields bordered by the latter have long been of the open type and separated from woodland for many years. In other parts of the country, enclosure of land was a more haphazard affair and continued over a protracted period so that the difference between the two kinds could be expected to be less clearcut. While there is no doubt that **indicator species** of plants can sometimes provide limited evidence of hedge origin, we need to be extremely cautious in applying this principle as a generalisation. Many ecological factors determine the potentiality for colonisation of a particular species, such as the nature of the soil and the range of climatic considerations. Thus a plant that is a poor colonist in one set of conditions may be successful in another. In parts of Wiltshire, for instance, shrubs such as field maple and dogwood are common in hedges planted during the last 400 years that have never been associated with woodland. Similarly, bluebells and primroses have been successful colonists during the last 20 years, their arrival being associated with a changing system of hedge maintenance. It follows that, before drawing conclusions from such data, careful checking is desirable against the relevant documentary evidence.

That living hedges may already have been in existence in the 12th century is suggested by an edict of Richard I to his tenants relating to his hunting activities, that the height of a hedge was not to exceed 4 feet 6 inches (1.3 m) so as to avoid impeding the movement of deer.[2]

13

The effects of the enclosures

As was indicated earlier, by far the most important factor determining the nature of our landscape has been economic. In the 13th century, the clearing of assarts and the establishment of other units of medieval enclosures, such as 'purprestures' and 'encroachments', brought a certain orderliness into the agricultural scene during a period of comparative prosperity. This was the first phase of the Enclosure movement whereby each village was provided by the local landlord with six areas of land – one for domestic purposes (houses, etc.), one for meadow (including hay), one for grazing and three for agriculture. Of these three, one was planted with spring corn, one with autumn corn and the third remained fallow. Hedges of various kinds undoubtedly played a part in delineating the different blocks of land. It must be emphasised, however, that the above scheme was an idealised one; in practice it was subject to innumerable variations depending particularly upon the whims of local landowners. But the three-field type of agriculture was to become typical of most areas of the country and remained so for the next 200 years. Reliable local records of this period are not easy to find. Most of those available from sources such as County Records Offices are printed, being copies of earlier documents that are often inaccurate, difficult to interpret in a modern context or even fakes.

By the 16th century radical changes in farming practice had begun and this period marks the second phase of the Enclosure movement. The expansion of the wool industry (coupled with a greater demand for meat as food) increased the profitability of producing sheep rather than crops. In many parts of the country this spelt the end of the open three-field system and proved catastrophic for the farming communities. Since it required fewer workers to tend sheep than to grow corn, widespread unemployment followed. Enclosures were universally unpopular in rural areas and even led to rioting. However, they were backed by numerous Acts of Parliament and the new agriculture was here to stay. With it came a change in the appearance of the landscape, since a prime need now was for fields with hedges that were stockproof. Some of the oldest hedgerows existing today date from this period. Although records exist of 16th-century Enclosure legislation, these can be exceedingly complex to study and difficult to understand. For those interested in trying for themselves, the titles of several good introductory texts are included in the Bibliography.

Like all adaptive processes extending over a wide area, the changes outlined above did not take place all at once, nor to the same extent. Constrasting the proportion of land enclosed by Act of Parliament in different English counties,[5] we see that whereas in the Midlands (Northants, Huntingdon, Rutland, Bedford and Oxfordshire) this ranged from around 45–50 per cent of the whole, in more remote districts such as the West Country (Devon and Cornwall) there were no Acts of Enclosure at all. It is significant that, particularly in Cornwall, many of the outlines of the medieval field systems are still visible today.

The third phase of the Enclosure movement dates from about 1750 until the mid-19th century, when the most extensive enclosure took place either by private arrangement or as a result of Parliamentary legislation. This involved the closing off of two very different kinds of ground: the old open field systems with their associated arable, and 'waste' (uncultivated ground) often referred to as common ground or 'commons'. COMMONS

Once again, economic factors determined the new direction in agriculture. The woollen industry was on the decline and the requirement was now to provide food for an increasing population, particularly in the urban areas. The large, irregular medieval field systems were subdivided into smaller more rectangular ones, each often bounded by a hedge, which was not necessarily always stockproof. It is often stated that the enclosures of this period, as in medieval times, destroyed much peasant agriculture and produced widespread misery among those who had depended on the land for a living, many of whom migrated to the cities. However, in some areas at least, this view may have been mistaken. Judging by the number of smallholdings that existed after enclosure, it may actually have increased the prospects of employment in some places,[5] although this may not have been true of the country as a whole. By the end of the 19th century the newly planted hedges, many of them based on hawthorn, had reached a mature state and the appearance of the countryside must have resembled closely the condition that we know today.

In the 20th century, and particularly over the last 25 years, the economics of agriculture have changed yet again, towards a greater emphasis on arable farming with high production levels resulting from the increased use of fertilisers and pesticides, and the employment of farm machinery such as combine harvesters of ever increasing size.[6] In such circumstances, small fields of around 3 ha (about 7 acres) that had previously housed livestock were no longer economic and needed to be increased by removal of hedges to about 8 ha (approximately 20 acres). At the upper

15

end of the scale there was also a limit to the size of a field judged to be economic. This is now considered to be about 120 ha (roughly 300 acres), an area large enough to accommodate any machines likely to be employed for arable cultivation in the foreseeable future.[7] Further enlargement would have disadvantages of two kinds: the waste of time in refuelling and reloading vehicles, and the ergonomic monotony of an unending furrow. The usual situation in Britain where machines are frequently employed in ones and twos is not comparable with that of the New World, where fields are far larger and many vehicles can work together. Once fields have attained their optimum size, there would seem to be no good reason for further hedgerow destruction. However, objections to the continual presence of hedges have also been voiced on other grounds, and these will be considered further in Chapter 6.

Changing hedge patterns – an example

Many of the features of the origin of hedgerows outlined in the previous pages are well illustrated in an excellent piece of research carried out by the Conservation Section of the Avon County Council Planning Department[8] on the small Manor of Englishcombe, near Bath (Avon), occupying an area of 709 ha (1750 acres).

Evidence of early occupation and medieval features is shown in the reconstructed map (Fig. 1.13a). This includes fine Romano-British sites, a Roman road and an Anglo-Saxon thoroughfare, the Herepath (or Harepath). The most impressive remains are of the Wansdyke, a large bank and ditch of uncertain origin. It could have been defensive or a political boundary, but it bears no relationship to manorial or parish boundaries. It has been variously dated from late Roman to early medieval. In the neighbouring parish of Priston, a document dated 1578 refers to Whiddlecombe Hedge – a parish boundary consisting of an earth bank and ditch that may well date from the Saxon period, although there are no records to prove this.

A reconstructed map of the area in the 14th century (Fig. 1.13b) shows the existence of typical open fields bounded by woodland from which they were probably derived. To the east, a considerable area of trees still existed, while the open field boundary may have been a 'dead' hedge of the kind illustrated in Figure 1.7. Remains of a ridge-and-furrow type of agriculture (p. 6) are clearly visible on the ground in places. The recon-

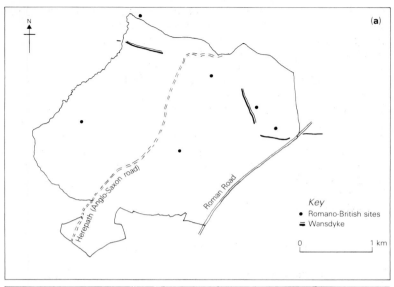

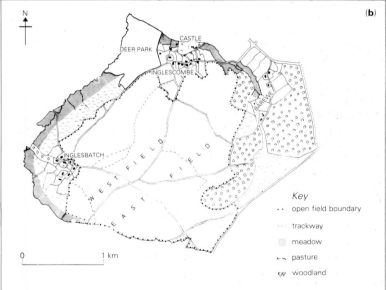

Figure 1.13 The origin of field patterns and hedge boundaries in the Manor of Englishcombe, near Bath, Avon:[8] (a) Romano-British and early medieval features; (b) reconstruction about 1300;

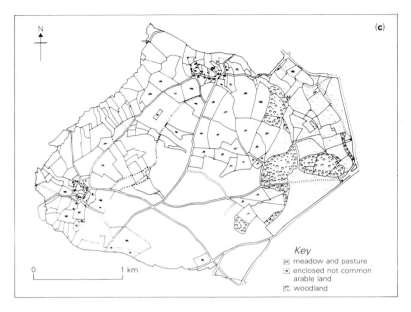

Key
⬚ meadow and pasture
▣ enclosed not common
    arable land
⬚ woodland

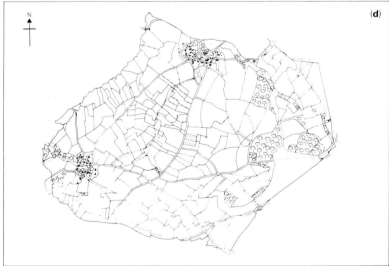

(c) reconstruction 1611; (d) William Simpson map of 1792; (e) existing
situation, 1982.

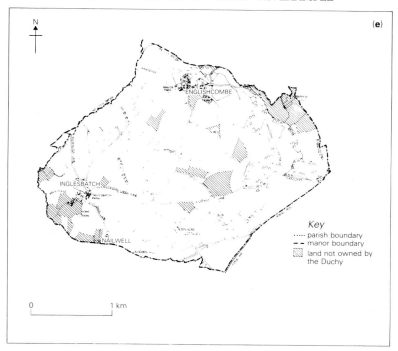

structed map for 1611 (Fig. 1.13c) shows the effects of the early enclosures, particularly in the west, with the narrow strips of fields grouped as furlongs (see p. 6). However, some open fields were still in evidence to the southeast and a considerable area of woodland persisted to the northeast. By 1792 (Fig. 1.13d) the whole area was enclosed by hedges, the small fields being predominantly strip-like.

But during the next half-century until about 1860, a radical change occurred in response to a return from wool production to arable farming and the consequent need for larger fields. This was the period of maximum hedge removal, a process that has continued at varying intensity until the present. Thus in the period 1973–82, about 15 hedges are recorded as having disappeared. The existing pattern of greatly enlarged fields is shown on the modern map in Figure 1.13e.

Interesting evidence of the woodland origin of many of the present-day fields is provided by their names. Thus an extensive area to the northeast called Estover was originally heavily wooded (Fig. 1.13b) – the name indicates that tenants' rights existed to take wood for a variety of purposes. Today, only a few small woods remain, such as Breach Wood and Vernham Wood (Fig. 1.13e); the remainder is agricultural land. Again, individual field names such as Ashes Hill, Woodleaze and Westwood strongly suggest a woodland derivation, possibly by assarting as long ago as the 12th century.

The origins of verges

By the end of the 18th century, the roads of England were in an unbelievably bad state, as we know from contemporary writers such as Jane Austen. In winter, potholes and mud abounded, and these conditions persisted into the early 19th century, when men like Telford and McAdam introduced a new technology of road construction, including a regular system of repair. One outcome of the new order was that carriageways became a good deal narrower, since it was no longer necessary for vehicles to dodge from side to side to avoid the major hazards. The process of change was gradual, and, as ground was relinquished between the edge of the road and its boundary (often a hedge), colonisation by plants took over, giving rise to the verges that we know today. Alongside main roads these could be as wide as 3 yards (3 m) or more, while on minor thoroughfares they often extended no more than about a foot (0.3 m) from the roadside. Following the advances in methods of road building and the vast increase during the present century in the amount and diversity of traffic, verges have come to assume ever increasing importance. In purely *material* terms, some of their main functions are:

(a) to provide added visibility for drivers at bends and corners;
(b) as places for vehicles to park in an emergency;
(c) as areas where road repair equipment and materials can be temporarily deposited;
(d) as places for drains and soakaways to remove surface water; and
(e) as a means of providing structural support to the road surface.

But verges also have other functions that are essentially *social*, such as:

(a) providing a visual link between a road and its surroundings;
(b) the separation of pedestrians and horse riders from motor vehicles;

20

(c) when they are broad, providing appreciable areas of country open to public access; and

(d) increasingly acting as significant reservoirs of plants and animals, particularly in areas where hedges have been removed – in this they complement the action of hedgerows.

The portion of a verge nearest the road is subject to constant disturbance due to such factors as the throwing up of mud during wet weather by passing vehicles and pollution caused by salting in winter and by exhaust gases such as compounds of lead. Further from the road, conditions are more stable and a rich community of herbaceous plants, both annuals and perennials, frequently grows up. As the process of ecological competition proceeds, ever larger species take over, often impeding the visibility of traffic at the height of summer. One of the problems facing the Local Authorities responsible for highway maintenance is to promote the safety of the public while respecting material and social considerations. As we shall see in Chapter 7, this is not easy and can all too easily lead to conflicts of interests where the fortunes of hedgerows and verges are concerned.

2

Age and diversity

As we saw in the previous chapter, some of our most ancient hedges and even a few verges may be as much as 800 years old. Dating these structures with any precision is not easy and it poses a fascinating challenge, which is not only instructive but may also be important, for instance where matters of ownership are involved. There is only one way of discovering for certain the age of a hedge. That is from documentary evidence. Sadly, all too often, such evidence does not exist and we are therefore driven to adopting less exact methods. The remainder of this chapter will be concerned with a critical appraisal of the principal procedures available to us at present.

Imagine a hedge planted by a farmer during the early 19th century consisting of a double row of hawthorns spaced 2 feet (0.6 m) apart (many of our existing hedgerows must have originated about that time in this manner). At first, there will have been considerable gaps at the base of the shrubs open to colonisation by other plants as their fruits and seeds were dispersed from elsewhere by wind or by animals such as insects and birds. These outside colonists will have been of three kinds:

(a) Herbaceous annual plants, including most of the typical garden weeds such as the chickweed, groundsel, shepherd's purse and certain grasses.

(b) Herbaceous perennials capable of accumulating food reserves to survive the winter, providing them with a flying start once conditions become favourable for growth. These include relatively slow hedgerow colonists such as bluebells, primroses and dog's mercury, and also less desirable and more rapid arrivals such as stinging nettles, dandelions and thistles.

(c) Woody perennials that do not have to die down in winter. These are shrubs and small trees, such as elder and holly, which, as they grow, are able to compete with hawthorn for a place in the hedge. Hedges frequently contain appreciable numbers of large forest trees such as oak. Some of these, like the hedges themselves, will have been derived from woodland, while others could have survived and grown from the seedling stage. But the majority, by far, will have been planted at the same time as the rest of the hedge (mostly in the 19th century) as is often indicated by their systematic and regular spacing.

The picture that emerges of a living hedge is therefore one of a dynamic, interacting collection of competing plant species. As time proceeded, many of the early colonists will have succumbed in competition with later arrivals for the essentials of life such as light, water and a supply of nutrients from the soil. Superimposed on all this is the external influence of man, in particular his methods of management, which can favour some species at the expense of others. Thus, the older a hedge, the greater the opportunity for different species to explore every existing opportunity for colonisation and establishment. In other words, the *diversity* of species present will tend to *increase* with *time*. In theory, therefore, it should be possible to use diversity as an index of age.

One of the problems of applying this apparently simple principle is that no two hedgerows are the same. The rates of change in their composition, for instance, vary greatly from one part of the country to another. Moreover, the presence of a wide variety of plants concentrated together inevitably attracts a comparably diverse collection of animals – herbivores, defoliators, parasites and the rest. Their densities and activities can also exert powerful effects on the rate of change. Other important variables with comparable effects are the range of plant species that originally composed the hedge (the shrubs planted were by no means only hawthorn and were frequently mixed species), the physical conditions, particularly the nature of the soil and climate, the kinds of maintenance applied (if any) and their frequency. All these factors will be considered separately in later chapters. Suffice it to add here that, bearing in mind the number of variables involved, it is hardly surprising to find that the dating of hedgerows using ecological evidence alone is subject to a considerable margin of error.

Dating hedges from subjective evidence

Earlier (p. 13) we saw how the presence of certain *indicator species* of plants can provide evidence of a hedge's ancestry. Bluebell (*Endymion non-scriptus*), dog's mercury (*Mercurialis perennis*) and primrose (*Primula vulgaris*) are all species occurring in or on the edge of woods. Their occurrence in hedges strongly suggests a woodland origin, possibly dating back to the assarts of the 12th to 14th centuries (p. 13). In some instances, this has been confirmed from documentary evidence.[4] On the other hand, we must not overlook the possibility of secondary colonisation at a later date, such as has certainly occurred in parts of Wiltshire, particularly by primroses, bluebells and dog's mercury.

Hawthorn as an indicator species

One of the most interesting and important indicator shrubs in hedgerows is hawthorn, of which there are two species. The commoner, *Crataegus monogyna* (Fig. 2.1), is widely distributed throughout Britain. The leaves are lobed and often deeply cut (Fig. 2.2), and the flowers are small and numerous, each usually having one style and one stone in the fruit. The stems have many

Figure 2.1 Hawthorn (*Crataegus monogyna*) in flower.

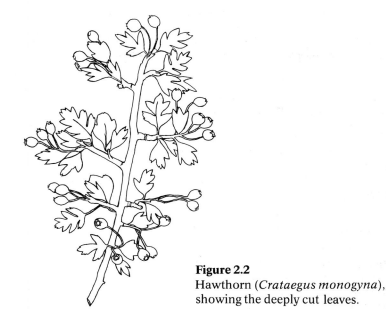

Figure 2.2
Hawthorn (*Crataegus monogyna*),
showing the deeply cut leaves.

spines. The growth form is also characteristic, particularly in woodland where it tends to grow upright to a small tree with few side branches. However, its principal habitats are sunlit open spaces, where it forms a bush. The second species is *Crataegus laevigata* (formerly *C. oxyacanthoides*), sometimes referred to as the Midland thorn. It is mainly a woodland species, less common than *C. monogyna*, preferring the clay soils of the Midlands and certain areas of the South. The leaf shape tends to be toothed but with relatively little dissection (Fig. 2.3). The flowers are fewer and larger than the former species, with two or more styles and fruits usually with two stones.

For the inexperienced, the two species are not as easy to separate in the field as might be imagined from the previous description. The most diagnostic feature is leaf shape, but here there is considerable variation, as can easily be determined by stripping the leaves from a single stem and arranging them in order of lobe-size. It will be found that there is a considerable overlap between the two species, as is indicated by the drawings of actual specimens shown in Figures 2.2 and 2.3. The situation is further

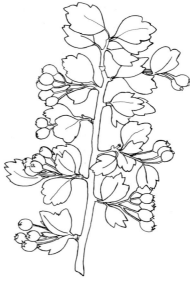

Figure 2.3 Midland thorn (*Crataegus laevigata*), whose leaves tend to be entire with little dissection.

complicated by the fact that, when they occur together, an appreciable amount of hybridisation occurs, and this leads to further variation and overlapping.

Detailed studies[9] of the distribution in hedgerows of *C. monogyna* and *C. laevigata* have enabled leaf indentation to be expressed as a ratio of the total lengths of indentation on one side of the leaf to the length plus the breadth of the leaf. Typical results for two pure populations in Horish Wood, Kent (*C. laevigata*) and Upchurch, Kent (*C. monogyna*) are shown in Figure 2.4. It will be seen that there is a considerable overlap between them within the leaf indentation range 0.15–0.20. Convincing evidence has also been accumulated to show that, provided clay is present, the more ancient a hedge, the more likely it is to contain a high proportion of *C. laevigata*. During the late Enclosure period of the 19th century and thereafter, there was evidently a widespread tendency to use *C. monogyna* varieties displaying increasing dissection of the leaves. The reason for this may have been partly aesthetic but also possibly related to the fact that leaf segmentation is correlated with the thorniness of the stem and hence with the effectiveness of the shrub as a stockproof barrier. The principle is well illustrated by data from hedgerows in the vicinity of an ancient road at Monk's Wood, Hunts., summarised in Figure 2.5. The portion of Saxon origin was found to contain both *C. monogyna* and *C. laevigata*, while the parts dating from late-19th century enclosures and the mid-20th century were almost pure *C. monogyna*. Interestingly, the degree of dissection of the leaves of *C. monogyna* had increased markedly with time, attaining a maximum in the 1962 planting. Hawthorn is a plant with a long life and when cut back in coppicing it has a capacity for throwing up new shoots from the base, which is why it has proved so valuable as a shrub for hedging. It could well be that plants growing in Roman times or even earlier are still alive today. Much remains to be discovered about the use of hawthorn species for the dating of hedgerows and woodland, and this could be a fertile field for further enquiry. Meanwhile, although the distribution of *Crataegus monogyna* and *C. laevigata* pro-

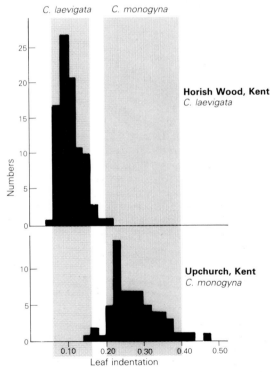

Figure 2.4 Comparison of leaf indentation in pure populations of *Crataegus monogyna* and *C. laevigata*.[9]

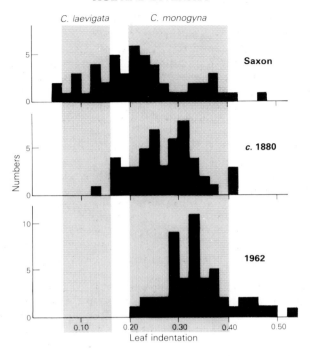

Figure 2.5 Leaf indentation in populations of *Crataegus* of different ages in hedges at Monk's Wood, Hunts.[9]

vides us with useful evidence of approximate antiquity and origin, it does not as yet give any more precise quantitative estimate of age.

Bramble as a possible indicator

The use of the predominant hedge shrubs as indicators of antiquity could well be developed further once we understand more about the nature of their variants. A typical example is the bramble (*Rubus futicosus*) where numerous subspecies have been described in Britain, possibly comprising as many as 387 distinct species. The reason for this extraordinary degree of variation can be explained if we look at the ways in which brambles reproduce. This is to a considerable extent by **apomixis** in which the plants form fruits and seeds without the need for fertilisation. More-

28

over, cross pollination between different individuals often fails altogether or produces malformed fruits in which only a few of the seeds are fertile. The situation in *Rubus* therefore differs from the majority of flowering plants, where cross pollination readily occurs between members of the same species, leading to off-spring with a range of variation that is more or less similar throughout the species' range. But, in brambles, each variant ('species') enjoys almost total genetic isolation from its neighbours.

The spread of these different forms within the localities where they occur is achieved by a second method of reproduction, which is entirely vegetative. When they are long enough, the stems bend over under their own weight and where the tips touch the ground, they root, forming the familiar loops that frequently trip up unwary walkers through woodland. Eventually, new aerial stems develop at the point of rooting. In this way it is quite common for the offspring of a single plant to cover a considerable area, all the offspring having an identical hereditary constitution (**clone**).

In theory, the older a site, the greater will be the opportunity for different bramble species to colonise it through the chance arrival of seeds. Diversity should therefore provide an index of antiquity. There is some evidence for the validity of this approach,[10] which could provide a useful means of determining the relative ages of different hedges provided they contain brambles.

Unfortunately, the identification of the different bramble species (sometimes referred to as **batology**, from the Greek word *Batos*, meaning 'bramble') poses considerable difficulties for the inexperienced since the criteria used are not easy to apply in practice. These include such features as leaf shape and colour, the shape, number and distribution of the spines on the stems and leaves, the colour of the stems and the presence or absence of glandular hairs. An additional problem is that some of these characters, such as stem colour, are influenced to a considerable extent by environmental factors, particularly light and shade. So we must conclude that, while the bramble dating of hedgerows may show promise for the future, in our present state of knowledge its widespread application as a reliable method is still no more than subjective and in the experimental stage.

Dating hedges from quantitative evidence

As we saw earlier (p. 23), apart from the influence of man, the most powerful ecological factors influencing the rate of change in a hedge are colonisation by outside species and their competition with ones already present. It follows that the greater the age of the hedgerow, the more varied should its flora become. This proposition has been tested[11] by selecting 227 hedges in different parts of the country whose date of origin could be gauged from documentary evidence with some degree of certainty, and estimating the number of species of shrubs occurring in lengths of 30 yards (27.4 m). A correlation coefficient of +0.85 was obtained, indicating a close positive relationship between the two variables. (A figure of +1 would have meant that a perfect linear correlation existed; 0 that there was no correlation; while a minus figure would have indicated an inverse relationship.[12]) An equation for estimating the age of a hedge from the number of shrub species in a 30-yard stretch is:

$$X = 100Y + 30$$

where X is the age of the hedge in years, and Y is the number of

Figure 2.6 A hedge of beech (*Fagus sylvatica*) on Exmoor (Somerset). The dense leaf canopy precludes colonisation by other shrub and tree species.

shrub species in a 30-yard (27.4 m) length. The procedure makes no claim to be more than an approximation, so in practice a sampling distance of 30 paces is quite accurate enough.

Bearing in mind the variations in the sequence and rate of change in hedgerows, it is not surprising to find that estimates of age derived from the equation are subject to appreciable error. On statistical grounds, it is estimated that the 95 per cent confidence limits lie within the range ±200 years. That is to say, the estimated age of a ten-species hedge will be $(110 \times 10) + 30 = 1130 \pm 200$ years. In other words for 95 per cent of such hedges, their age lies between 1330 and 930 years. Similarly, a five-species hedge could be aged between 780 and 380 years.

The procedure is applicable in all areas where, traditionally, single species were planted. These include much of the South and Midlands. Further north, hedges tend to be replaced by stone walls, while on acid soils, colonisation of roadside banks is frequently dominated by gorse (*Ulex europaeus*). Again, some hedge-forming species such as beech (*Fagus sylvatica*) quickly form a dense leaf canopy almost impervious to light, thus precluding colonisation by other competitors. Such hedges are characteristic of Exmoor and, although the oldest were planted there little more than 150 years ago, there is, as yet, little sign of any appreciable penetration by other shrubs (Fig. 2.6).

Practical problems in hedge dating

The method of dating outlined above rests on the assumption that the rate of accumulation of woody species of plants is correlated positively with hedgerow age. If we are to evaluate the procedure more closely, we need to ask two questions:

(a) What evidence is there that changes do, in fact, take place in the composition of hedges?
(b) To what extent do estimated ages of different hedgerows agree with evidence from documentary records, both over wide areas and in more localised situations?

Evidence for change

In contrast to our detailed knowledge of the nature of changes in well defined natural habitats such as chalk downland, comparatively little is known about comparable sequences in hedgerows. This is partly because the subject has been somewhat neglected but is also partly due to the difficulty of ascertaining with any certainty the number of shrub species originally present. Again, methods of management of which few records exist may well have played a part in influencing hedge composition, for instance the well known practice of removing elder when hedges are laid. Paradoxically, elder is more frequent in hedges that have been managed than in those that have not.[11] This suggests that certain kinds of management (perhaps all) encourage regeneration from plant remains or colonisation by propagules (mainly fruits and seeds) from elsewhere, or both.

Two other indicator species may be useful in helping to date hedges. Field maple (*Acer campestre*) is a constituent of many hedgerows on both alkaline and neutral soils, but it is unusual to find it in conjunction with only one or two other shrub species, i.e. in young hedges. It begins to appear when four or more woody species are present, in other words when the age of the hedge has reached at least 400 years. Spindle (*Euonymus europaeus*) behaves in a somewhat similar manner, but tends to come in later than field maple and is characteristic of hedges 600 years old or more. As an indicator species it has the disadvantage of preferring calcareous soils (chalk and limestone), so its distribution is somewhat restricted. Other species with a wide degree of soil tolerance that could well prove useful indicators of suc-

Figure 2.7 Wayfaring tree (*Viburnum lantana*), an early colonist of hedgerows on calcareous soils.

cession include hazel (*Corylus avellana*) and holly (*Ilex aquifolium*), while on calcareous soils the wayfaring tree (*Viburnum lantana*) (Fig. 2.7) and dogwood (*Cornus sanguinea*) are conspicuous colonists, and in some places seem to establish themselves as part of the hedgerow community quite early in its existence.

Error in age prediction

The original sample of 227 hedges from which the predictive formula was derived covered a considerable area of the country and was therefore heterogeneous in terms of composition, age and origin. Bearing this in mind, it is both surprising and encouraging that the method of estimating hedgerow age outlined above has stood the test of time so well. Subsequent studies have supported the general contention that an approximately linear relationship exists between the age of a hedge and the number of shrub species composing it. A typical example is summarised in Figure 2.8 and shows the results of a survey carried out by schools in different parts of the country involving a total of 118 records. The dots in the body of the diagram represent the number of hedges in

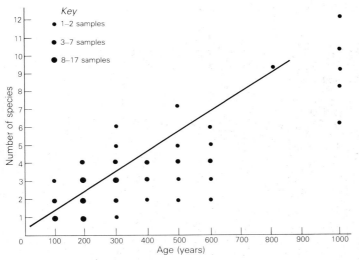

Figure 2.8 Results of a survey of the relationship between the age of hedges (as shown in old documents) and the number of shrub and tree species they contain, per 30 m length of hedge.[69] The survey was carried out by schools in different parts of the country.

Table 2.1 Documentary and estimated ages of three kinds of hedge in Shropshire.[21] All figures are to the nearest 100 years.

Origin of hedge	Documentary age range (years)	Average shrub species per 30 yards (27.4 m)	Estimated age range (years)
assart	900–600	5.5	800–400
piecemeal enclosure	500–300	4.7	700–300
commons enclosure	200–100	5.7	900–500

each group, and there is a clearly linear relationship between estimated and documentary age.

However, anomalies sometimes arise, as is illustrated in Table 2.1, which summarises data obtained from the vicinity of three villages in Shropshire, samples consisting of about 50 hedge lengths each of 30 yards (27.4 m). While estimates for the assart hedges and those of 15th–17th century origin are in close agreement with documentary evidence, those for the late 18th and 19th centuries diverge by a minimum of 300 years. Either the incorporation of new shrub species took place much more rapidly during this period (for which there is no evidence) or the method of hedge planting underwent radical change. Fortunately, agricultural records of the time provide us with the likely answer. In order to avoid the expense of purchasing the traditional hedging shrub, hawthorn, it became common practice among farmers when planting new hedgerows to use any woody species that happened to be growing nearby, such as holly, hazel or field maple. For the estimation of age, diversity of species was therefore fictional. This only serves to underline the point made earlier that, before accepting such estimates, they should always be checked, if possible, against reliable documents.

For students of hedgerows, the most usual requirement will be not to cover a wide area but rather to concentrate on a more restricted situation, such as a single parish, where documentary evidence in the form of church and diocesan registers, parish council records, private estate documents and tithe maps are frequently available. Just such a study has been carried out[13] in the parish of Church Broughton, Derbyshire, where the age of hedges in the vicinity could be established reliably from documents within 100 years or less. The results are summarised in Figure 2.9. As in previous studies, there is a significant effect of age on the number of woody species present, with hedges accumulating an average of between 0.46 and 1.47 species per

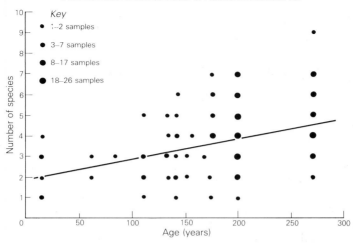

Figure 2.9 Relationship between the number of woody species and mean age for a number of hedges in one parish whose date of origin was known from old documents.[13]

century. In other words, the rule of thumb estimate of one new species per 100 years appears to hold good.

Other points of interest emerge from this study, which could well repay repetition elsewhere. For instance, the composition of hedgerows appeared to vary appreciably according to their location. While the number of woody species in roadside samples averaged 4.75, that for hedges between fields was 4.06, representing a statistically significant difference ($P<0.01$). Again, the mean values for brookside and garden hedges (4.64 and 4.67) were somewhat higher than for field hedge samples (4.27), representing a significant difference between them ($P<0.05$). Another important finding related to the influence of past management procedures (or the lack of them) on the floral composition of hedges. It has frequently been claimed that management can be an appreciable factor influencing both the nature and the rate of change. In the Church Broughton area, it was possible to separate hedges that had been managed by trimming or laying (p. 146) (comprising some 415 samples) from those that had not been managed (453 samples). Subsequent analysis revealed no significant difference between the two groups in either diversity of species or their individual frequency. Again, this is the kind of investigation that needs to be repeated elsewhere.

The findings just described have important implications for

studies of hedgerow dating based on small localised areas such as parishes. At this intensity of sampling, variations in composition between hedges occupying different localities such as roadsides, gardens and between fields become much more apparent and must be taken fully into account. Over a wider area these effects tend to cancel one another and are no longer of such significance. In any local study the first step, therefore, is to construct a calibration graph of documentary age against number of species covering as many hedges in as wide a range of circumstances as possible. As we have seen, if concentration is focused only on one kind of hedge, such as that of roadsides, conclusions for the area as a whole are likely to be misleading. It has been suggested[14] that a preliminary sample of 12 such hedges is sufficient, but if we are to accommodate the total range of variation, a larger number is required – of the order of 50 or more, depending on the diversity of terrain. Moreover, in order to take account of the variation within a particular kind of hedge, a calibration graph should be used to date *groups* of hedges thought to be of similar age rather than individuals.

Finally, as we saw earlier, it is always possible that hedges with a high shrub content may have been planted that way, a possibility worth bearing in mind when consulting documentary evidence. But provided the number of samples in an area is high and calibration graphs show clearly a relationship between the number of shrub species and age (which need not necessarily be linear), such deviations should not invalidate the findings overall.

Trees as indicators of hedgerow age

Mature trees such as oak often form a significant component of hedgerows, as is illustrated in Fig. 2.10. Following the catastrophic effects of Dutch elm disease, the stumps of felled elm trees are now all too common a feature of hedges, particularly in the South. Counting the annual rings will give an accurate estimate of the age of such trees. If this is greater than that of the hedge in which they occur (judged by the number of shrub species), this suggests that the area may once have been woodland which was later felled. This is particularly likely if several trees of the same age occur in a single hedge. If, on the other hand, the trees in a hedge appear to be younger than the hedge itself, this indicates that they were later colonists. The problem is to estimate with reasonable precision the age of a tree without having to cut it down.

Figure 2.10   Mature trees such as oak (*Quercus robur*) frequently form a significant component of hedgerows.

On the basis of some 20 000 records, the Forestry Commission has concluded[15] that the majority of larger tree species exhibit a remarkably uniform pattern of growth judged by the size of the girth (measured 1 m from ground level). Young trees tend to grow somewhat faster than older ones but on average an increase in girth of 2.5 cm (1 inch) a year is a good approximation. The 'one inch rule' applies only in situations, such as most hedgerows, where the tree has been able to develop a full crown and is situated in the open. Under the competitive conditions of woodland, the rate of annual increase is nearer 1.3 cm ($\frac{1}{2}$ inch). Many of the smaller hedgerow trees never aspire to the growth rate of the larger species. These include apple, pear, holly, hawthorn, rowan and whitebeam,[16] where a girth increase of 1.3 cm ($\frac{1}{2}$ inch) a year is nearer reality.

An example of the way in which the estimated age of trees can throw light on the history of a group of hedges is illustrated in Figure 2.10, part of an area of farmland near Broughton Gifford, Wiltshire. At 1 m from the ground, the girth of the oak in the foreground was 310 cm (124 inches). The girths of five other trees in the same hedge ranged from 240 cm (96 inches) to 330 cm (132 inches), suggesting that all were planted at the same time, about 100 years ago. Sampling the hedgerows in the vicinity, 21 lengths of 30 paces each gave an average shrub count of 1.2 and therefore an estimated age of $(110 \times 1.2) + 30 = 162$ years. The situation is

37

somewhat equivocal on account of the margin of possible error. However, there is strong evidence to suggest that the hedges and oak trees are the same age and were probably planted at the same time, a conclusion supported by early 19th century maps of the area.

The limitations of using trees as indicators of the age of hedges are obvious enough in that they can only cover a relatively short timespan. But used in the sort of context outlined above, they can provide valuable confirmatory evidence and also highlight problems in age estimation that might otherwise have been overlooked.

Verges: sizes and shapes

Compared with hedgerows, most existing verges are of relatively recent origin and are seldom more than 100 years old. It has been estimated[17] that the extent of roadside vegetation in England and Wales, which consists mostly of verges, amounts approximately to 0.415 ha of maintained land per kilometre of road (1.65 acres per mile). Such areas provide valuable habitats for plant and animal communities. Using the Department of the Environment/Ministry of Transport figure of 225 450 km (140 100 miles) for the total of country roads, the area of roadside vegetation works out at 93 560 ha (231 190 acres). To this must be added an estimated further 3645 ha (9000 acres) of banks and verges bordering motorways, giving a total overall of approximately 97 200 ha (240 000 acres).

Comparatively little is known about the widths of verges in different parts of the country. That these vary greatly is evidenced by data from the counties of Somerset and Glamorgan, which are summarised in Table 2.2. Both counties are somewhat atypical in that they possess large numbers of low-category roads with narrow verges. There are also striking differences between them. Thus the average width of verges beside trunk roads in Glamorgan is the same as that of the numerous unclassified roads in Somerset. The extreme narrowness of the verges beside the main roads of Glamorgan could be explained by the fact that many are associated with industrial and housing areas, or run through valleys.

As is becoming increasingly clear, the width of a roadside verge is more than just of academic interest. Frequently a verge adjoins a flanking hedgerow, the two possessing numerous herbaceous plant species in common. Many of these provide food for a

Table 2.2   Width of verges by class of road in Somerset and Glamorgan.[17] Class I roads are A category; class II roads are B category; class III roads are minor roads with 4.3 m of metalling or over; unclassified roads have less than 4.3 m of metalling or are untarred.

County	Class of road	Distance (km)	(miles)	Average width of verge (cm)	(inches)
Somerset	trunk	188	117	188	75
	I	655	407	130	52
	II	473	294	123	49
	III	2526	1569	108	43
	unclass'd	3016	1873	98	39
	total	6858	4260		
Glamorgan	trunk	98	61	98	39
	I	419	260	35	14
	II & III	679	422	83	33
	unclass'd	1014	630	60	24
	total	2210	1373		

variety of birds and insects, some beneficial to the farmer and all of interest to naturalists. Once a hedge has been removed for farm improvement, as has all too frequently happened in the past, the verge is all that remains of this valuable reservoir of plant and animal life.

Diversity of verge vegetation

There is much evidence that the primary factors determining the composition of hedgerows are the sequence and rate of plant penetration. The age of a hedge is therefore a function of the number of shrub species it contains and vice versa. Physical factors, such as geology and climate, are of secondary importance, as are the effects of maintenance. The situation in verges is quite different. Most are of comparatively recent origin and changes, although they certainly occur, are determined by other influences. Of these, by far the most important are cutting, usually with mechanical flails (p. 148), and treatment with herbicides. The significance of these procedures and their differing effects need not concern us here but will be discussed fully in the context of conservation in Chapter 7.

Apart from the effects of maintenance, other factors also contribute to the diversity of plants and animals that colonise verges.

Figure 2.11 Two aspects of a typical roadside hedge: (a) southern aspect with a luxuriant vegetation dominated by meadowsweet (*Filipendula ulmaria*); (b) northern aspect bordering a meadow with a soft rush (*Juncus communis*).

One of the most important of these is aspect. In general, south-facing verges are more diverse and therefore of greater interest than north-facing. This is because they are better illuminated and the plants live in a more variable climate. The principle is well illustrated in Figure 2.11, which shows the two aspects of a typical roadside hedge. Figure 2.11a is the southern aspect, and shows that the verge is luxuriant and dominated by two species, the compact rush (*Juncus conglomeratus*) near the road, and meadowsweet (*Filipendula ulmaria*) towards the hedge. On the north facing side (Fig. 2.11b), which borders a meadow, soft rushes and a variety of grasses predominate, while meadowsweet is absent.

Another significant factor influencing the composition of verge communities is disturbance of the ground, particularly that bordering the road. Most of this consists of physical upheaval by passing traffic, but chemical pollution also plays a part, such as run-off from the salting of roadways in winter. Some plants are adapted to these conditions and even flourish in them. When the soil is alkaline, a particularly successful colonist of roadsides is the greater plantain (*Plantago major*), illustrated in Figure 2.12. The large pieces missing from the leaves are evidence of feeding

Figure 2.12   Greater plantain (*Plantago major*) colonising a roadside verge – an area of disturbed ground. The pieces missing from the leaves provide evidence of feeding by the garden snail (*Helix aspersa*) and black slug (*Arion ater*).

Figure 2.13   White deadnettle (*Lamium album*) growing on an inner verge.

by the garden snail (*Helix aspersa*) and the large black slug (*Arion ater*). Moving inwards from the roadside, the nature of the habitat becomes increasingly dominated by the ditch (if present) and the hedge, which may exert a strong shading effect. In general, therefore, the conditions away from the road tend to be more stable and humid than at the edge, and open to intense competition by a wide variety of plants. One species that is often conspicuously successful in the South is the white deadnettle (*Lamium album*) (Fig. 2.13).

A simple way of estimating the diversity of plants in a verge is to lay down a belt **transect** across it at right angles to the road. This can consist of two pieces of string laid parallel, 1 m apart. Unit areas are then stepped off at regular intervals along the transect and the numbers of each species noted. Figure 2.14 records the results obtained from a belt transect 1 m wide with counts made at 0.5 m intervals. From this it will be seen that the habitat preferences of the two species studied were different. While the plantain flourished on disturbed ground at the edge of the road (Fig. 2.12), the white deadnettle (Fig. 2.13) colonised the less extreme conditions nearer the hedge.

A more comprehensive but quite simple way of determining the diversity of a plant community, such as that colonising a verge, is to estimate the numerical relationship between the total

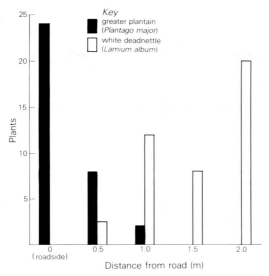

Figure 2.14 The distribution of the greater plantain (*Plantago major*) and white deadnettle (*Lamium album*) on a roadside verge.

number of plants present and the number of individuals per species. The necessary information can be obtained from a belt transect or from a **quadrat** – an area of known size, often a square metre (1 m²), either marked out with string or measured by a light wooden frame. Various methods are available for calculating the diversity index,[12] one of the simplest being the formula:

$$D = \frac{N\,(N-1)}{\Sigma\,n\,(n-1)}$$

where D = diversity index, N = total number of individual plants, n = number of individuals per species, and Σ indicates summation. Thus, in the belt transect of a verge, we might obtain the distribution of broad-leaved plants shown in Table 2.3. This would give a diversity index:

$$D = \frac{94(94-1)}{22(22-1) + 12(12-1) + 16(16-1) + \text{etc.}} = \frac{8742}{1432} = 6.1$$

One of the advantages of this method of gauging plant diversity over the previous one is that identification of each species is unnecessary. All that is required is a means of distinguishing one

43

Table 2.3 Typical broad-leaved plants found in a belt transect of a verge.

Index	Species	Number
1	greater plantain (*Plantago major*)	22
2	dandelion (*Taraxacum* sp.)	12
3	white deadnettle (*Lamium album*)	16
4	lesser celandine (*Ranunculus ficaria*)	21
5	cowslip (*Primula veris*)	4
6	yarrow (*Achillea millefolium*)	8
7	common knapweed (*Centaurea nigra*)	11
	total	94

species from another, for which an index of numbers or letters is adequate.

In a natural community subject to increasing complexity, we would expect that, on average, the diversity index would tend to increase year by year as a result of competition between species and fresh colonisation from without. However, the conditions facing verge communities are so unnatural that successive estimates of the diversity index in the same area are likely to tell us little about the extent of natural changes. But they can provide a useful means of monitoring the effects of different kinds of maintenance. Suppose we found on a subsequent visit to the same area that the value of D had dropped from 6.1 to say 4.5, and later to 3.1. This could serve as an objective warning that artificial treatment was gradually reducing the verge community to a state of uniformity.

3

The ecology of hedgerows
and verges: plants

An outstanding feature of both hedgerows and verges is their infinite variety. They vary not only in their composition but in the diverse situations in which they occur. Figure 3.1 illustrates a section of a typical hedge with north and south aspects, bordering a thoroughfare on one side and a field with an agricultural crop on the other. This is a common arrangement but there are numerous variants on the theme. For instance, many hedges are in the midst of farmland and separate one area of agricultural land from another. Again, a feature such as a verge may be much expanded in circumstances like a motorway embankment but greatly contracted in a cutting, when it may be absent altogether.

But in spite of their varying topography, verges represent distinct kinds of plant and animal habitats, consisting of a mosaic

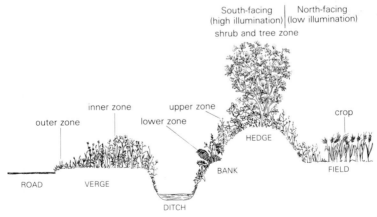

Figure 3.1   Generalised section of a hedgerow with north and south aspects, bordering a road on one side and a field on the other.

of localities each associated with a particular range of vegetation. Although the structure of this is often complex, investigation shows that the overall pattern of the distribution of species exhibits a considerable degree of uniformity. This suggests the existence of certain unifying and overriding influences. As in hedgerows, the most powerful factor affecting the survival and spread of different verge-dwelling species is the nature and extent of management. Where this is absent, taller plants are at an advantage. These include the coarser grasses, such as couch (*Agropyron repens*), cocksfoot (*Dactylis glomerata*), Yorkshire fog (*Holcus lanatus*) and false oat (*Arrhenatherum elatius*), large umbellifers, like cow parsley (*Anthriscus sylvestris*) and hogweed (*Heracleum sphondylium*), and other strongly growing species, such as the meadow buttercup (*Ranunculus acris*). Frequent cutting, flailing or grazing encourages the finer-leaved grasses, notably common bent (*Agrostis capillaris*) and the fescues (*Festuca* spp.). It also favours rosette-forming species, like creeping buttercup (*Ranunculus repens*), greater plantain (*Plantago major*) and dandelion (*Taraxacum* sp.).

Perhaps one of the most significant outcomes of the recent studies on plants associated with hedgerows and verges is the finding that a major proportion of them are species known to flourish on fertile soils where they are able to compete successfully for growth with other plants. Of recent years, the large-scale application of nitrogenous fertilisers to agricultural land has become common practice and it may well be that the translocation by leaching and drainage of nutrient-rich water has had an appreciable effect on the composition of the adjacent roadside flora.

Zonation in hedgerows and verges

In the light on what has been said above, any scheme for dividing hedgerows and verges into distinct zones might be regarded as no more than a rough approximation. Nonetheless, such a scheme can provide a useful basis for description and is the plan that will be adopted here.

Verges

These are divisible into two parts, which are often fairly clearcut and easily identifiable. The outer zone is frequently no more than 15 cm (6 in) wide, although it can extend inwards for as much as three times this distance. It is characterised by pollution from the adjoining road and compaction, disturbance and erosion by the wheels of vehicles and the feet of pedestrians. As might be expected, it supports a characteristic flora and fauna. The total width of verges varies greatly (see Table 2.2) depending upon the area of the country and the class of road. The span of the inner zone can therefore range from less than 1 m (3 ft) to four times that distance or even more. In general, the further away from the road, the more stable the environment becomes.

Ditches

These are frequently absent, as on the north facing side in Figure 3.1. Any water accumulating at the foot of the bank either soaks away through the ground or runs into drains associated with the adjoining field or roadway. Where a ditch exists, there is a wide range of alternatives from a shallow gulley carrying water in winter but drying out in summer, to small permanent waterways sometimes flowing but often static. An important factor influencing the ecology of ditches is the degree and frequency of maintenance. Periodic clearance can quickly convert the environment from a diverse set of ecological conditions into virtual lifelessness.

Banks

Hedges are usually planted on banks of earth ranging from several metres high alongside road cuttings to less than 1 m (3 ft) on flat surfaces. Where ditches are deep, the effect of a bank can be greatly enhanced. Some banks were constructed in medieval times or even earlier and represent former boundaries to property, so that they long pre-date the hedgerows now growing on them. Like verges, hedge banks can be divided roughly into two zones (see Fig. 3.1). The lower zone is dominated by the ditch (where present) and also the ground at the base of the hedge and the inner zone of the verge. The upper zone is more intimately associated with the trees and shrubs forming the hedge, particularly their roots. The distinction between the two zones varies greatly. Where banks are high and well illuminated, it is often quite clear, but on low banks, particularly those facing north, the dividing line is far less obvious. Nonetheless, zonal classification is useful in attempting to analyse the distribution of the different plant communities.

47

Shrub and tree zone

This is composed predominantly of woody bushes, their roots penetrating into the bank or deeper soil below and exerting a considerable effect on the local environment. As has been shown[11] (p. 23), there is often a positive correlation between the age of a hedge and the number of shrub species it contains, and this provides a useful method of dating within certain limits. Also present in hedges are numbers of mature trees or saplings, either planted, derived from previous woodland, or later colonists from outside. Again, their girth can sometimes provide useful supplementary evidence in judging the age of a hedge and its origin (p. 36).

Environment and plant distribution

Although the hedgerow environment is a variable one, some variables exert a far greater effect on plant distribution than others. Predominant among these is aspect. In outlining the plant communities typical of the various zones, it is clearly impossible to budget for every eventuality, and the description that follows will concentrate on the well illuminated, i.e. mainly south-facing, aspect. This is not to say that some species occurring on the south side may not be found on the north also. In the previous description of the different environments it was emphasised that a considerable overlap occurs between them. It is to be expected, therefore, that plants listed as occurring in one context may also be found in another.

An important factor of the soil environment is the presence or absence of calcium. This usually occurs as calcium carbonate in the form of chalk or lime. The majority of hedgerow plants show a wide degree of soil tolerance. However, some have a particular affinity for calcium (**calcicole**) while others have a low tolerance of it (**calcifuge**). In the species lists that follow, these preferences are denoted as C+ and C− respectively. Finally, it must be emphasised that the lists of species typical of particular habitats make no pretence at completeness. They are intended only as a general guide to the *kinds* of plant communities likely to be found in different places, and to assist in distinguishing one hedgerow zone from another. For detailed lists of roadside species, reference should be made to the various County floras, which frequently include useful summaries.

Zoning hedgerows and verges in the way described earlier

serves to highlight the fact that, ecologically, they represent a heterogeneous set of environments. In this chapter, an attempt will now be made to analyse these environments a step further.

Verge

Outer zone

The soil here is adjacent to the material composing the road and is greatly influenced by it. An essential feature of all prepared thoroughfares is that their base must be well drained. This capacity for drainage extends to the neighbouring soil, with the result that the outer fringe of a verge is always drier than the rest. Again, the frictional effects of passing traffic and pedestrians can be considerable, causing continual disturbance to the rooting systems and green parts of potential plant colonists. It is hardly surprising, therefore, that relatively few species are able to tolerate such a disturbed environment.

A particular problem has arisen on major roads in winter due to the greatly increased use of salt (sodium chloride) to reduce icing (about 1½ million tonnes a year). In the most highly salted areas, the salinity can reach the level of a saltmarsh, promoting colonisation by salt-loving plant species (**halophytes**).[18,19] In general, salt affects verges in two ways. First, the increased salinity produces a soil environment that many of the usual colonists, including several common grasses, are unable to tolerate. As a result they die, leaving bare patches of earth. Detailed records from four different counties[18] show that these die-back zones extend to an average of 0.4 m (1.2 ft) from main roads and can cover 1 m (3 ft) or more. Again, sodium ions are known to play an important part in flocculating clay, causing the fine particles to clump together, thereby improving crumb structure, aeration and drainage. But if sodium is in excess, the process of flocculation is upset, the crumb structure of the soil breaks down and any clay present becomes compacted in impermeable layers, thus reinforcing the deleterious effects of vehicle wheels and pedestrian trampling.

All the species shown in Table 3.1 are well adapted to conditions of periodic drought and disturbance. The greater plantain (*Plantago major*) has been illustrated growing in a typical outer verge habitat (Fig. 2.12). One of the more conspicuous species is scentless mayweed (*Matricaria perforata*), which occurs everywhere (Fig. 3.2).

In many ways, the situation in the outer zone of verges is

Table 3.1 Some typical species found in the outer zone of the verge.

Species	1	2	3	4	5	6	7	8	9	10	11	12
greater plantain (*Plantago major*)					●	●	●	●				
ribwort plantain (*P. lanceolata*)				●	●	●	●	●	●	●	●	
pineapple mayweed (*Chamomilla suaveolens*)						●	●	●	●	●	●	●
scentless mayweed (*Matricaria perforata*)				●	●	●	●	●	●	●		
red bartsia (*Odontites verna*)						●	●	●	●	●		
creeping cinquefoil (*Potentilla reptans*)					●	●	●	●	●			
corn spurrey (*Spergula arvensis*) C−						●	●	●	●	●		
daisy (*Bellis perennis*)			●	●	●	●	●	●	●	●		
annual meadowgrass (*Poa annua*)	●	●	●	●	●	●	●	●	●	●	●	●
perennial ryegrass (*Lolium perenne*)					●	●	●	●				
wall barley (*Hordeum murinum*)					●	●	●					

Flowering period (month)

Figure 3.2 Scentless mayweed (*Matricaria perforata*), a common colonist of disturbed ground.

comparable to that of heavily trodden tracks across grassland or down country lanes. The differences between the plants colonising the compacted ground and those on either side can be striking, and provide an interesting and worthwhile subject for study.

Inner zone

Unlike the outer strip, the inner area is relatively free of pollution from the road and other effects of traffic. Conditions are more stable and soil composition, particularly humidity, is dominated by the ditch (if present) and the shading effect of the hedge. This zone frequently supports a luxuriant growth of plants, the main pressures upon them being the various forms of maintenance, to which we will return to Chapter 7.

Although their preference is for the ecological conditions provided by verges, nearly all the species in Table 3.2 colonise the lower zone of banks from time to time. Dense growths of cow parsley (*Anthriscus sylvestris*) with their umbels of white flowers (Fig. 3.3) are a familiar feature of most hedgerows in early summer. White deadnettle (*Lamium album*) is another conspicuous verge colonist (Fig. 2.13), which can usually be found in flower every month of the year (particularly from March to November).

Figure 3.3 Cow parsley (*Anthriscus sylvestris*), a feature of many verges in early summer.

Table 3.2 Some typical species found in the inner zone of the verge.

Species	1	2	3	4	5	6	7	8	9	10	11	12
hogweed (*Heracleum sphondylium*)				●	●	●	●	●	●	●	●	
cow parsley (*Anthriscus sylvestris*)				●	●	●						
mugwort (*Artemisia vulgaris*)							●	●	●			
common knapweed (*Centaurea nigra*)						●	●	●	●			
thistles (*Cirsium* spp.)						●	●	●	●			
silverweed (*Potentilla anserina*)					●	●	●	●	●			
wild carrot (*Daucus carota*)							●	●				
hawkweeds (*Hieracium* spp.)								●	●	●		
common toadflax (*Linaria vulgaris*)							●	●	●	●		
bird'sfoot trefoil (*Lotus corniculatus*)						●	●	●	●	●		
field forget-me-not (*Myosotis arvensis*)				●	●	●	●	●	●	●		
rest harrow (*Ononis repens*)						●	●	●	●	●		
goatsbeard (*Tragopogon pratensis*)						●	●	●	●			
campions (*Silene* spp.)						●	●	●	●	●		
white deadnettle (*Lamium album*)	●	●	●	●	●	●	●	●	●	●	●	●
clover (*Trifolium* spp.)						●	●	●	●	●	●	●
timothy (*Phleum pratense*)						●	●	●				
smooth meadowgrass (*Poa pratensis*)					●	●	●	●				
yarrow (*Achillea millefolium*)						●	●	●	●	●	●	

Ditch

Ditches can be divided roughly into three categories. Some are relatively shallow and cleared only occasionally. During the summer they are often dry, while in winter the depth of water can be 0.5 m (1½ ft) or more. Again, a ditch may be relatively deep and contain standing water all the year round. The environment then resembles a small pond with a layer of air-free mud at the bottom with a foul smell. A third possibility is when a ditch carries flowing water, becoming a small stream, often a tributary of a larger waterway. The eroding force of the current washes away any accumulated particles of soil and decaying organic matter, leaving a bed that is firm and stony. At the edge, the current is less strong and here banks of mud sometimes build up, providing an attractive rooting medium for plants.

Dry in summer

Ditches that dry out in summer provide an unstable environment for colonisation by plants. Few species except horsetails (*Equisetum* spp.) can tolerate the muddy conditions in the middle of a ditch and the majority are rooted in the firmer ground at the

Figure 3.4 Comfrey (*Symphytum officinale*) occurs as white- and mauve-flowered forms and prefers damp locations.

53

Table 3.3 Some typical species found in ditches that are dry in summer.

Species	Flowering period (month)											
---	1	2	3	4	5	6	7	8	9	10	11	12
common comfrey (*Symphytum officinale*)					●	●						
marsh woundwort (*Stachys palustris*)						●	●	●	●	●	●	
lesser burdock (*Arctium minus*)							●	●	●			
hemp agrimony (*Eupatorium cannabinum*)							●	●	●			
wintercress (*Barbarea vulgaris*)				●	●	●	●	●				
marsh thistle (*Cirsium palustre*)						●	●	●	●			
common horsetail (*Equisetum arvense*)				●								
great willowherb (*Epilobium hirsutum*)						●	●	●	●			
marsh bedstraw (*Galium palustre*)						●	●	●				
hogweed (*Heracleum sphondylium*)				●	●	●	●	●	●			
common valerian (*Valeriana officinalis*)						●	●	●				

sides. Many of those in Table 3.3 are also characteristic of the banks of streams and ponds. One of the most widespread species is comfrey (*Symphytum officinale*), which occurs as mauve- and white-flowered forms (Fig. 3.4) and is of possible commercial interest on account of the high protein content of its tissues. Incidentally, it also provides the food plant for the larvae of one of the most attractive of our day-flying moths, the scarlet tiger moth (*Panaxia dominula*). In fertile conditions, the growth of some of these ditch-side plants during the summer can reach formidable proportions, extending a metre high or more. Typical examples are the great willowherb (*Epilobium hirsutum*), hemp agrimony (*Eupatorium cannabinum*) and meadowsweet (*Filipendula ulmaria*), which frequently dominate other competitors and exert a strong shading effect on the environment below.

With permanent static water

With the exception of duckweed, all the species in Table 3.4 are rooted in mud, the most striking being marsh marigold (*Caltha palustris*), illustrated in Figure 3.5. Beside the ditch the ground is wet but relatively firm. Here the colonists are similar to those of ditches that dry out in summer (see above). In the natural conditions of ponds and lakes, the tendency is for mud to accumulate year by year as successive generations of plants die down in winter. The process is particularly noticeable at the water's edge. As the water becomes progressively shallower, conditions change in a landward direction. For instance, plants adapted to rooting in mud, such as brooklime (*Veronica beccabunga*) and watercress (*Nasturtium officinale*), are replaced by those

Table 3.4 Some tyical species found in ditches with permanent static water.

Species[a]		Flowering period (month)											
		1	2	3	4	5	6	7	8	9	10	11	12
duckweed (*Lemna* spp.)							●	●	●				
fool's watercress (*Apium nodiflorum*)								●	●				
marsh marigold (*Caltha palustris*)				●	●	●	●	●	●				
meadowsweet (*Filipendula ulmaria*)							●	●	●	●	●		
brooklime (*Veronica beccabunga*)						●	●	●	●	●	●		
water forget-me-not (*Myosotis scorpioides*)						●	●	●	●	●	●		
water figwort (*Scrophularia auriculata*)							●	●	●	●	●		
watercress (*Nasturtium officinale*) C+						●	●	●	●	●	●	●	
hemlock waterdropwort (*Oenanthe crocata*)							●	●	●	●			
starwort (*Callitriche stagnalis*)						●	●	●	●	●	●		
water crowfoot (*Ranunculus aquatilis*)						●	●	●	●	●	●	●	

[a] All these species, with the exception of duckweed, are rooted in mud. Starwort is submerged. Duckweed is floating.

Figure 3.5 The marsh marigold (*Caltha palustris*) grows on the edge of still water with its roots in mud.

adapted for drier conditions, like comfrey (*Symphytum officinale*) and great willowherb (*Epilobium hirsutum*). This kind of succession from a water community towards a land one is known as a **hydrosere**. Left unattended, hydroseres inevitably develop in ditches. However, in practice this seldom happens, since the main purpose of periodic clearance is to prevent obstruction and improve drainage.

With permanent running water

The species in Table 3.5 are predominantly submerged and rooted in the substratum or on the surface of stones. Starwort possesses floating leaves as well as submerged ones, while the flowers of water crowfoot float on the surface of the water. Ditches of this kind are usually small streams connecting with larger tributaries (Fig. 3.6) and their ecology is typical of flowing water.[12] At the edge and out of the main stream, mud accumulates to varying depths and this supports the characteristic flora of ditches with permanent static water summarised in Table 3.4, while colonists of the bank are similar to those in ditches that are dry in summer (Table 3.3).

Table 3.5 Some typical species found in ditches with permanent running water.

Species	Flowering period (month)
	1 2 3 4 5 6 7 8 9 10 11 12
river water crowfoot (*Ranunculus fluitans*)	● ● ● ● ● ● ●
starwort (*Callitriche stagnalis*)	● ● ● ● ●
Canadian pondweed (*Elodea canadensis*)	● ● ● ● ●
willow moss (*Fontinalis antipyretica*)	[capsules rare]

Figure 3.6 A typical small stream at the base of a hedge.

Bank

Like the verge, this can be divided for convenience into two zones (Fig. 3.1), although the distinction is often unclear, particularly when the bank is low.

Lower zone

Two features tend to dominate this area. The proximity of the ditch results in a relatively high soil humidity and an abundance of organic material (**humus**) from dead plants. In the absence of a ditch, the bank may border a thoroughfare, for instance if it runs through a shallow cutting. While the soil may still be relatively moist compared with that higher-up, increasing proximity to a road can exert an overriding effect in increasing desiccation, disturbance and pollution. Problems of colonisation by plants are then similar to those associated with the outer zone of a verge. A second important influence is that of the shrubs above, which can exert a powerful shading effect, tending to increase humidity. Aspect will also play a significant part in this respect.

The damp, shaded conditions in the lower zone of a bank favour colonisation by mosses and a variety of ferns. Among flowering plants (Table 3.6), the most striking indicator species is lords and ladies (*Arum maculatum*), with its conspicuous pale green hood (**spathe**) and purple or yellow finger-like structure (**spadix**) above the tiny male and female flowers. The arrow-shaped leaves are variable, some having small dark-brown patches and others not (Fig. 3.7). The character is evidently inherited, so that all the leaves on one plant are the same. The

Figure 3.7 Polymorphism in the leaves of lords and ladies: some have dark-brown blotches, others have none.

Table 3.6 Some typical species found in the lower zone of the bank.

Species	Flowering period (month)											
	1	2	3	4	5	6	7	8	9	10	11	12
lords and ladies (*Arum maculatum*)					●							
hart's tongue fern (*Asplenium scolopendrium*)							●	●				
black spleenwort (*A. adiantum nigrum*)					●	●	●	●	●	●		
male fern (*Dryopteris filix-mas*)							●	●				
polypody (*Polypodium vulgare*)						●	●	●	●			
cut-leaved cranesbill (*Geranium dissectum*)					●	●	●	●				
herb robert (*G. robertianum*)					●	●	●	●	●			
marsh bedstraw (*Galium palustre*)						●	●					
red campion (*Silene dioica*)					●	●	●					
rough chervil (*Chaerophyllum temulentum*)				●	●	●						
lesser celandine (*Ranunculus ficaria*)							●	●				
creeping buttercup (*R. repens*)					●	●	●	●				
hedge woundwort (*Stachys sylvatica*)							●	●				
sweet violet (*Viola odora*)		●	●	●								
meadow fescue (*Festuca pratensis*)						●						
common St John'swort (*Hypericum perforatum*)								●	●	●		
primrose (*Primula vulgaris*)			●	●	●							
bluebell (*Endymion non-scriptus*)			●	●	●							
dandelion (*Taraxacum* spp.)			●	●	●	●						
herb bennet (*Geum urbanum*)					●	●	●	●	●			

Figure 3.8 Polymorphism in the primrose (*Primula vulgaris*): (a) *pin* flower in which the mouth of the corolla is blocked by the stigma; (b) *thrum* flower in which the opening of the corolla is encircled by the five anthers.

proportions of the two (**polymorphism**) vary in different parts of the country, ranging from about 30 per cent spotted in the South to only 2 per cent in the North. The reasons for this change are still unknown and this could provide an interesting topic for further investigation. A different kind of polymorphism, which is better understood, occurs in the primrose (*Primula vulgaris*), where two kinds of flowers exist. In one (*pin* type) the mouth of the flower (**corolla**) is blocked by the pin-like head of the stigma; in the other (*thrum* type) the opening of the flower is encircled by five anthers (Fig. 3.8). Again, the two forms are inherited and have been shown to be a device for promoting cross-pollination by insects[20] and reducing self-pollination. Other common flowering species include the campions (*Silene* spp.), creeping buttercup (*Rannuculus repens*) and dandelion (*Taraxacum* spp.).

Upper zone

As in the lower zone, shading by shrubs and trees will tend to increase soil humidity. However, this is the main location for the roots of bushes, which will have the reverse effect. On balance, the upper zone of a bank is usually drier than the lower and this can play a decisive part in determining the pattern and distribution of the plant populations (Table 3.7).

Figure 3.9 Greater stitchwort (*Stellaria holostea*), an adaptable species found commonly in the upper zone of hedge banks.

Table 3.7 Some typical species found in the upper zone of the bank.

Species	1	2	3	4	5	6	7	8	9	10	11	12
greater stitchwort (*Stellaria holostea*)				●	●	●						
common chickweed (*S. media*)	●	●	●	●	●	●	●	●	●	●	●	●
yarrow (*Achillea millefolium*)						●	●	●	●	●	●	
betony (*Stachys officinalis*)						●	●	●	●	●		
hedge woundwort (*S. sylvatica*)						●	●	●	●	●		
wild basil (*Clinopodium vulgare*) C+							●	●	●			
marjoram (*Origanum vulgare*) C+							●	●	●			
feverfew (*Tanacetum parthenium*)						●	●	●	●			
garlic mustard (*Alliaria petiolata*)				●	●	●	●	●				
cleavers (*Galium aparine*)						●	●	●				
lady's bedstraw (*G. verum*)							●	●				
dove's foot cranesbill (*Geranium molle*)				●	●	●	●	●	●			
ragwort (*Senecio jacobaea*)						●	●	●	●	●		
golden rod (*Solidago virgaurea*) C−							●	●	●			
wall barley (*Hordeum murinum*)						●	●					
hairy brome (*Bromus benekii*)						●	●	●				

As was emphasised earlier, the distinction between the various hedge zones is somewhat arbitrary and by no means always clearcut. This is particularly true of banks where the situation is greatly influenced by their depth, aspect and the nature of the hedging shrubs and trees above. A number of the familiar plants growing in the drier upper zones are also frequent colonists of the inner zone of verges, where conditions are often somewhat similar. A species that is usually restricted in its distribution to hedge banks is the greater stitchwort (*Stellaria holostea*), illustrated in Figure 3.9.

Climbers and ramblers

A small but important group of plants are rooted in the bank and adapted for climbing (Table 3.8), using tendrils (white byrony) or twisting (e.g. hedge bindweed). Many of these species such as ivy (Fig. 3.10) produce fruits that provide an important source of food for birds such as mistle thrushes during the winter. One of the most elegant species of climbers is the hedge bindweed (*Calystegia sepium*) (Fig. 3.11). Another is old man's beard (*Clematis vitalba*) (Fig. 3.12). This latter figure shows the flowers and fruits, from which the plant derives its English name. In conclusion, it is worth noting that the two bryonies, both of which produce red berries in autumn, are unrelated. White bryony (*Bryonia dioica*) belongs to the gourd family (Cucurbitaceae) while black bryony (*Tamus communis*) is our only representative of the yams (Dioscoreaceae).

Table 3.8 Some typical species of climbers and ramblers found rooted on banks.

Species	Flowering period (month)											
	1	2	3	4	5	6	7	8	9	10	11	12
Herbaceous												
white bryony					●	●	●	●	●			
(*Bryonia dioica*)												
hedge bindweed						●	●	●	●			
(*Calystegia sepium*)												
hop							●	●	●			
(*Humulus lupulus*)												
black bryony					●	●	●	●				
(*Tamus communis*)												
Woody												
old man's beard							●	●	●			
(*Clematis vitalba*)												
ivy									●	●	●	
(*Hedera helix*)												
honeysuckle						●	●	●	●	●		
(*Lonicera periclymenum*)												
bittersweet					●	●	●	●	●			
(*Solanum dulcamara*)												

Figure 3.10 Fruits of ivy (*Hedera helix*), an important source of food for birds such as thrushes in winter.

Figure 3.11 Hedge bindweed (*Calystegia sepium*), one of the most elegant climbers in hedgerows.

Figure 3.12 Old man's beard (*Clematis vitalba*), another common climber: (a) the flowers; (b) the fruits, from which the plant derives its name.

Shrub and tree zone

The nature of this zone is influenced to a considerable extent by the kinds of shrub species originally planted. Changes in composition, as we have seen (p. 23), can take place in a fairly predictable manner, but there is still much to learn about the factors governing the rate at which they occur. Perhaps surprisingly, methods of maintenance seem to exert less effect on hedge composition than was at one time supposed. Geology and soil composition determine the presence or absence of certain shrub and

Table 3.9 Some common species of shrubs found in hedgerows.

Species	Flowering period (month)											
	1	2	3	4	5	6	7	8	9	10	11	12
hawthorn (*Crataegus monogyna*)					●	●						
midland thorn (*C. laevigata*)					●	●						
hazel (*Corylus avellana*)	●	●	●	●								
elder (*Sambucus nigra*)						●	●					
dogwood (*Cornus sanguinea*) C+					●	●	●					
blackthorn (*Prunus spinosa*)				●	●							
wild privet (*Ligustrum vulgare*)						●	●					
holly (*Ilex aquifolium*)					●	●	●	●				
spindle (*Euonymus europaeus*)					●	●						
wayfaring tree (*Viburnum lantana*) C+				●	●	●						
guilder rose (*V. opulus*)				●	●							
roses (*Rosa* spp.)						●	●					
barberry (*Berberis vulgaris*) C+					●	●						
bramble (*Rubus* spp.)					●	●	●	●				

Table 3.10   Some common species of trees found in hedgerows.

Species	|	*Flowering period (month)*										
	1	2	3	4	5	6	7	8	9	10	11	12
field maple *(Acer campestre)*					●	●						
ash *(Fraxinus excelsior)*				●	●							
oak *(Quercus* spp.)				●	●							
English elm *(Ulmus procera)*			●	●								
sycamore *(Acer pseudoplatanus)*				●	●	●						
crab apple *(Malus sylvestris)*					●							
wild cherry *(Prunus avium)*				●	●							
beech *(Fagus sylvatica)*				●	●							
whitebeam *(Sorbus aria)* C+					●	●						
mountain ash *(S. aucuparia)* C+					●	●						
willow *(Salix* spp.)			●	●								

tree species (calcicoles and calcifuges) and hence their geographical distribution, but the influence on hedges of small local variations in the environment seems to vary from one locality to another.

In Tables 3.9 and 3.10, although shrubs and trees are separated, in the context of hedgerows all the commoner tree species are frequently found as bushes derived from saplings maintained at hedge height by regular cutting. A typical example is field maple *(Acer campestre)*, which generally occurs in this form.

Reference has been made already (p. 24) to hawthorn as by far the most important of all hedgerow shrubs. The two species, *Crataegus monogyna* and *C. laevigata* (Figs. 2.2 & 2.3), have a characteristic distribution both in time and space, and can provide evidence on the probable age of hedges, particularly those of more ancient origin. Elder *(Sambucus nigra)* (Fig. 3.13) is a shrub that, if not cut back, can grow to a small tree of about 10 m (30 ft). It relishes hard treatment and this no doubt explains its

Figure 3.13 Elder (*Sambucus nigra*), a shrub with a capacity for colonising disturbed ground: (a) in flower; (b) the black fruits.

3.14 Blackthorn (*Prunus spinosa*) occurs in both species-poor and species-rich hedges: (a) in flower; (b) the fruits (sloes), conspicuous in autumn.

frequent occurrence in hedgerows. However, its capacity for colonising disturbed ground (it frequently occurs in the vicinity of badger setts) and its relatively short life probably explain why it is usually found in hedges with a small variety of other species, indicating that they are either of recent origin or occupying impoverished soil. Ash (*Fraxinus excelsior*) is one of the commonest hedge-forming trees and if left undisturbed can attain a height of 40 m (120 ft). Together with rose (*Rosa* spp.) and blackthorn (*Prunus spinosa*) (Fig. 3.14), it occupies a middle position as regards colonisation, occurring in both species-poor and species-rich hedges. By contrast, hazel (*Corylus avellana*), field maple (*Acer campestre*) and dogwood (*Cornus sanguinea*) tend to be restricted to hedges with a high species density. This suggests not only that they are good colonisers but also that they have been widely used in the past for the planting of mixed hedgerows.

As was emphasised elsewhere,[21] the differential adaptability of shrub and tree species has important implications for a theory of dating based on the assumption that hedges acquire new species at a more or less constant rate (p. 23). As colonisation proceeds, the probability of new arrivals establishing themselves must eventually decline as the availability of habitats decreases. The tendency of different shrubs to colonise hedgerows of differing ages probably accounts for the approximately linear relationship between age and diversity that has been shown to exist.

Finally, it should be noted that nearly all the shrubs listed in the table form conspicuous fruits (mostly coloured red or black) and these provide an important source of food for birds in autumn and winter. The implications of this for the distribution of different species will be considered further in the next chapter.

4

The ecology of hedgerows and verges: animals

The primeval vegetation of Britain was mainly deciduous woodland, most of which has since been cleared to meet the ever expanding needs of human existence. As forests contracted, their characteristic plants were faced with changing environmental conditions, including increased illumination. Some of the woodland species were able to adjust to the new environment and have survived in hedgerows but extended their range only slowly; others succumbed, their place being taken by sun-loving forms.

For animals, the situation was somewhat different. As woods disappeared and hedges grew up, these provided a logical extension of the ecological conditions to which the woodland faunas had been accustomed. Hedges also provided opportunities for many animals to extend their range, thereby reducing the pressures of competition. Evidence of this is particularly marked among mammals and birds, where the majority of species habitually occurring in hedgerows are also found in woods.

Mammals

Of the 28 species of British lowland mammals, 14 are commonly found in hedgerows and breed there.[22] Of these, all except the common rat are associated with woodland. The 14 commonest hedge-dwelling mammals are summarised in Table 4.1, together with their habitats and feeding habits. For convenience, they can be divided into two groups: the larger species, including the fox, badger, rabbit, stoat, weasel, hedgehog and mole; and the smaller ones, typified by the rodents and shrews.

71

Table 4.1 Habitats and foods of some common hedgerow mammals.

Species	Habitat	Omnivore	Carnivore	Insectivore	Herbivore	Diet
red fox (*Vulpes vulpes*)	Burrows (earths)		●			rabbits, rodents, birds, large insects (e.g. beetles), carrion, berries
badger (*Meles meles*)	burrows (sets)	●				rabbits, rodents, earthworms, much vegetable material (e.g. plant roots, acorns)
rabbit (*Oryctolagus cuniculus*)	burrows (warrens)				●	any green vegetation, particularly young shoots
stoat (*Mustela erminea*)	vegetation		●			rodents, young rabbits, sitting birds
weasel (*M. nivalis*)	vegetation		●			rodents, young rabbits, sitting birds; can climb trees
hedgehog (*Erinaceus europaeus*)	vegetation			●		insects, earthworms, slugs
mole (*Talpa europaea*)	burrows			●		insect larvae and other arthropods, earthworms

Species	Nest / shelter				Food
common rat (*Rattus norvegicus*)	burrows	●			earthworms, insects, molluscs, vegetable material (e.g. grain)
field vole (*Microtus agrestis*)	vegetation and tunnels		●		grasses and sedges
common vole (*M. arvalis*)	vegetation and tunnels		●		grasses and sedges
bank vole (*Clethrionomys glareolus*)	vegetation and tunnels		●		variety of soft vegetation
woodmouse (*Apodemus sylvaticus*)	vegetation		●		seeds of all kinds
common shrew (*Sorex araneus*)	vegetation			●	insects, spiders, woodlice, snails, some plant material (e.g. seeds)
pygmy shrew (*S. minutus*)	vegetation			●	insects, spiders, woodlice, snails, some plant material (e.g. seeds)

Larger mammals

In most of Britain, the red fox (*Vulpes vulpes*) is our only large terrestrial carnivore. Its colonisation of hedge banks is usually identifiable by the type of burrow (earth), which is considerably larger than that of a rabbit, and also by the characteristic droppings in the vicinity. Incidentally, it is worth noting that foxes sometimes occupy the disused setts of badgers, which can be a source of surprise to unsuspecting badger watchers! Unlike the badger, the fox is a solitary animal, mainly nocturnal in habit but occasionally active by day. Although an occupant of woodland, it is not averse to visiting streets and gardens in search of food.

The badger (*Meles meles*) advertises its presence in woods and hedges by its remarkable burrowings (setts), consisting of a number of holes about 20 cm in diameter and several metres apart. The excavated soil can reach extraordinary proportions and in older setts often amounts to several tonnes. Such disturbed conditions favour colonisation by a characteristic range of plants, one of the most frequent being elder, which is often a good indicator of the presence of badgers. As will be seen from Table 4.1, the animal is a true omnivore and seems to devour almost anything. It is an attractive creature and has been much studied, if only as a suspect for spreading bovine tuberculosis. One of the best accounts of its mode of life is that by Ernest Neal.[23]

The rabbit (*Oryctolagus cuniculus*) is often common in hedgerows and its presence can easily be established by the characteristic burrows, which conform to no particular pattern, and also by an abundance of spherical black droppings. The species is strongly social and mainly active at night, although colonies can frequently be observed at dusk. For a detailed account, reference should be made to the monograph by Sheail.[24] Before the advent of myxomatosis in 1953, the annual crop of rabbits in Great Britain was estimated to be 60–100 million, with densities ranging from 50 per hectare (20 per acre) at the highest level to about 5 per hectare (2 per acre) as an average. With the exception of a few localities, densities are now far lower. Rabbits eat a wide variety of vegetation, particularly the more nutritious kinds, a single animal devouring as much as 0.5 kg (1 lb) of fresh vegetation per day. It is small wonder that farmers regard them as pests.

The stoat (*Mustela erminea*) and weasel (*M. nivalis*) are our two smallest carnivores and their identification is sometimes confused. The stoat can be distinguished by its reddish brown parts, white underside and slender body not more than 30 cm (1 ft) long. The tail is relatively long with an obvious *black* tip. The weasel is much smaller and the size of a young rat, about 18 cm (7 in) long. The tail is short and has no black tip. Both are agile predators and well adapted by virtue of their shape and rapidity of movement to pursue their quarry through dense vegetation. Their diet is predominantly animal, mainly rabbits and small rodents. But they are also effective climbers and this enables them to prey upon nesting birds and their eggs and nestlings.

The hedgehog (*Erinaceus europaeus*) is the best loved of all the hedgerow mammals, chiefly on account of its ready relationship with man. Although essentially a woodland species, it is a common occupant of hedges, probably more so than is often realised. It appears to be particularly numerous in vegetation bordering human habitations. Although primarily an insectivore (see Table 4.1), its addiction to bread and milk makes it an easy animal to observe at close quarters and to breed in captivity. Like the badger, it quickly adjusts to a high level of illumination at night, which makes observation all the easier. The arrival of say three or four individuals at a food source each night may suggest that they belong to one or two families. But marking has shown that, in fact, as many as 14 different animals may be involved. This is best done with a patch of quickly drying cellulose paint applied with an aerosol spray (the kind used for touching up the paintwork of cars works well and lasts for several weeks before it is rubbed off). When surprised, the creature's usual reaction is to roll up into a tight ball and this provides a good opportunity for marking. Another endearing characteristic is the variety of grunts and snorts that it emits as it goes about its business, which are clearly audible and therefore advertise its presence in the vicinity.

The mole (*Talpa europaea*) is another woodland mammal that has secondarily colonised almost every kind of terrestrial habitat including hedges, although its preference is for more open ground. Being a burrower, it is seldom seen but is nonetheless abundant in some areas, particularly farmland, where there are usually high densities of earthworms and soil arthropods, which constitute its main items of food. Attempts to estimate the size of mole populations by relating density to the number of molehills have not been particularly successful but the most accurate average figures we have for grassland are about 10 per hectare (4 per acre) in winter, rising to double that number in summer.

Rodents and shrews

The rest of the mammals commonly found in hedgerows are summarised in Table 4.1 and are all relatively small, the largest being the common rat (*Rattus norvegicus*). This is an animal closely associated with human habitations and frequenting the less attractive parts of the environment, such as drains, rubbish dumps and unemptied dustbins. Nonetheless, it is a versatile feeder, which explains its frequent occurrence in hedgerows, particularly those bordering agricultural crops. In an ecological study of the lynchets on Portland Bill, Dorset (Fig. 1.5), extensive rat runs were found along the grass banks leading to periodic caches of food. This consisted almost exclusively of grain (no doubt obtained from an adjacent corn field) and the shells of the white-lipped snail (*Cepaea hortensis*), which abounded in the area.[25]

The remainder of the common hedgerow mammals consists of voles, mice and shrews, all small creatures that seldom move far from their established headquarters. The extent of this movement can be gauged to some extent by trapping using the Longworth type of trap.[12] This consists of two parts, a chamber in front containing the bait (oats are particularly attractive) and one behind filled with bedding such as straw for warmth in cold weather. Quantitative results obtained in this way are, however, always suspect and must be interpreted with due caution on account of the variable responses to traps by different individuals. Some animals are trap-shy and shun traps altogether, no matter how attractive the bait used. Others soon become accustomed to being caught and return again and again. It is, therefore, quite posssible for 10 successive captures in a particular trap to be all of the same animal!

Voles and mice are all predominantly herbivores, typified by the bank vole (*Clethrionomys glareolus*) and woodmouse (*Apodemus sylvaticus*) illustrated in Figure 4.1. Their normal behaviour is to run through the vegetation, often in shallow tunnels. But they are also capable of climbing, and this is particularly evident in the autumn, when they devour the fruits of shrubs, such as rose-hips. A characteristic behaviour pattern is to gnaw diagonally and cleanly across a rose-hip stem just below the fruit.[26] Mice tend to remove and eat the seeds, discarding most of the flesh, while voles do the reverse, devouring the flesh alone. With a little practice this behaviour can provide a useful means of estimating fruit predation by voles and mice. However, it must be remembered that by far the greater proportion of predation on

76

Figure 4.1 Typical hedgerow species of voles and mice: (a) bank vole (*Clethrionomys glareolus*); (b) woodmouse (*Apodemus sylvaticus*).

hedgerow fruits in autumn and winter is due to birds such as blackbirds, song thrushes and fieldfares.

Among the mammal species habitually captured by trapping in hedgerows[27] are the common shrew (*Sorex araneus*) and pygmy shrew (*S. minutus*) – the smallest of the British mammals. These are both mainly insectivores (see Table 4.1) but the fact that they are attracted to a bait of oats indicates that their diet includes some plant material as well. However, if you want to catch shrews, by far the best bait is said to be catfood!

Finally, it is worth noting that the density of small mammals in hedgerows can fluctuate seasonally to a marked degree, particularly when in close proximity to agricultural crops, which can provide an alternative source of food. The extent of migration varies from place to place, but species such as the bank vole, once established in a hedge, seldom stray more than about 5 m from it.[27]

Birds

Out of 91 recognised species of British birds, about 14 are commonly found in hedgerows and breed there. These are listed in Table 4.2 together with their foods and habitats. Like the mammals, the majority of bird species have strong woodland associations, hedgerows representing an extension of their accustomed environment. A comparison was made of the density of bird populations and the number of species on farmland that had never been enclosed and was bordered by banks and dykes and on farmland that had been enclosed and so possessed many hedges.[28] This showed that the density of birds per 1000 yards (914 m) on the farm without hedges was 8.3, while with hedges it amounted to 20.5. Again, on open fields, only five species were recorded, whereas on enclosed land there were eight.

As was emphasised in the previous chapter, the kind of ground enclosed by hedges is highly variable, so deciding what species constitute an average bird population of hedgerows presents some difficulty. A survey of the birds of farmland conducted by the British Trust for Ornithology concluded that the commonest species were the blackbird, skylark, hedge sparrow, chaffinch, robin, whitethroat, song thrush and yellowhammer. All of these are familiar colonists of hedges with the exception of the skylark, which prefers open country. One more species needs to be added to the list, namely the wren, an almost universal occupant in many parts of the country.

In Table 4.2 are summarised some of the commoner birds found in hedgerows together with their principal foods, also feeding and nesting habits. With one exception, all are residents, the only summer visitor being the whitethroat (*Sylvia communis*) (Fig. 4.2). The majority of these hedgerow species are relatively small. Since body area increases as the square of the

Figure 4.2 Whitethroat (*Sylvia communis*), the only summer migrant regularly found in hedgerows.

Table 4.2 Some birds commonly found in hedgerows, and their foods and habitats.

Species	Food	Trees (upper branches)	Trees (trunks, holes)	Bushes	Herbs (Low Ramblers)	Ground
Resident						
wood pigeon (*Columba palumbus*)	young plants and seeds, particularly cultivated	N,F				F
wren (*Troglodytes troglodytes*) +	insects, some plant material		N,F (ivy)	N,F		F
hedge sparrow (*Prunella modularis*) +	insects, tender plant material			N,F		F
robin (*Erithacus rubecula*) +	insects, tender plant material			F		N,F
blackbird (*Turdus merula*) +	molluscs, insects, berries			N,F		F
song thrush (*T. ericetorum*) +	molluscs (particularly snails), berries			N,F		F
blue tit (*Parus caeruleus*)	insects, buds of plants	F	N	F		
great tit (*P. major*)	insects, buds of plants		N	F		
long-tailed tit (*Aegithalos caudatus*)	insects, buds of plants			N,F		
house sparrow (*Passer domesticus*)	seeds, fruits, human domestic waste			N,F		
chaffinch (*Fringilla coelebs*) +	buds, fruits, tender plant material	N,F		F		

Species	Food			
bullfinch (*Pyrrhula pyrrhula*)	buds, fruits, tender plant material		N,F	
greenfinch (*Carduelis chloris*)	buds, fruits, tender plant material	N,F	N,F	F
goldfinch (*C. carduelis*)	seeds, particularly thistles		N,F,	F
linnet (*Acanthis cannabina*)	mainly seeds		N,F	
yellowhammer (*Emberiza citrinella*) +	mainly seeds		N,F	
Summer migrants				
sedge warbler (*Acrocephalus schoenobaenus*)	insects			N,F
garden warbler (*Sylvia borin*)	insects		N,F	
blackcap (*S. atricapilla*)	insects		N,F	
whitethroat (*S. communis*) +	insects		F	N,F
willow warbler (*Phylloscopus trochilus*)	insects		F	N,F
chiffchaff (*P. collybita*)	insects		N,F	N,F

+, Commonest species: N, nesting; F, feeding.

linear dimensions but volume increases as their cube, it follows that species such as the wren with a high ratio of surface to bulk will suffer a comparably large loss of heat during winter. This has somehow to be made good if they are to maintain their body temperature and survive. In fact, during periods of severe cold, we know that species such as wrens, goldcrests and blue tits are the first to succumb. Viewed in this context, it is significant that all the residents in hedges eat a diversity of food; even species that are predominantly insectivorous include vegetable material in their diet. By contrast, whitethroats and their allies (see Table 4.2) eat insects and practically nothing else, which helps to explain their need to migrate during our winter to warmer climates where insect populations are more abundant.

The fact that land enclosed by hedges is of many kinds serves to highlight the findings of some observers[29] that, while certain common bird species may predominate, nonetheless many other kinds of association are possible, some of them rather unexpected. For instance, near Cambridge the nightingale is a bird of hedges rather than woodland, presumably because most of the woods in the area are of beech with little or no shrub vegetation. Again, one of the commoner birds of hedgerows in south Warwickshire is the magpie, its success being correlated with the number of large and unmanaged hawthorn hedges, which provide both food and nesting sites.

Ecological factors and bird colonisation

Considering the importance of hedgerows in supporting a dense and diverse bird fauna, it is perhaps surprising that so little attention has been paid to the study of the ecological factors concerned. One of these is the nature and quantity of the food supply. As an experiment,[23] nine marked stems of rose bushes were selected, carrying 184 hips, and their gradual disappearance recorded between September and February. The results are summarised in Figure 4.3, from which it will be seen that all except nine hips were removed by birds, mostly fieldfares (*Turdus pilarum*), blackbirds (*T. merula*) and song thrushes (*T. ericetorum*).

One of the most extensive studies of a bird species in hedgerows[30] is that of the yellowhammer (*Emberiza citrinella*) (Fig. 4.4). About one-sixth of all population density variations was found to be associated with differences in the lengths of hedges and their number per unit area. In general, the more hedgerows, the larger the yellowhammer populations. There

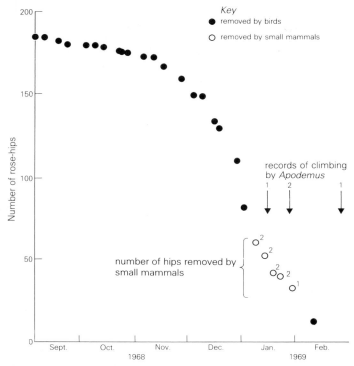

Figure 4.3 Removal of rose-hips by birds and mammals from branches in a roadside hedge, September 1968–January 1969.[27]

were also significant differences in bird density between hedges containing trees and those without them. Evidently, the presence of song posts was an important ecological factor. On the other hand, it was clear that song posts were not the only habitat factor of importance, for the presence or absence of lines of trees along field boundaries made no difference to population densities. Thus, ecological factors influencing colonisation by yellowhammers included both hedge and tree components.

Comparable studies have been carried out by the Game Conservancy[31] on the nesting preferences of the partridge (*Perdix perdix*), which tends to shun open fields in favour of hedges. Here again, colonisation is influenced by both the quality and quantity of the habitat. Partridge territories tend to be large and the optimum length of a nesting habitat is estimated at 8 km/km² (35 yards per acre). Below this level, there is a progressive fall-off

Figure 4.4 Yellowhammer (*Emberiza citrinella*), one of the most extensively studied of hedgerow birds.

in breeding density, which becomes dramatic at 5 km/km² (22 yards per acre). In February and March it is desirable that plenty of dead grass should have accumulated at the base of the hedge covering at least 25 per cent of the bank. Access by stock, particularly sheep, should be prevented and cutting should not be carried out between March and July. Although partridges do not require large amounts of nesting cover, there is evidently a basic minimum level that must obtain for successful breeding to take place.

Finally, it must be emphasised that bird populations in hedgerows are dynamic systems in a constant state of flux. In the larger species particularly, such as blackbirds and song thrushes, exchange is taking place constantly with the surrounding environment of fields and thoroughfares. For smaller species such as the tits, it has long been known that hedges act as corridors for movement from one habitat and feeding ground to another.[32] Evidence for such movements can easily be obtained with the expenditure of a certain amount of patience and careful observation. One of the arguments against the removal of hedgerows is that such movement is no longer possible and this leads to a concentration of populations in areas of woodland, the rise in density resulting in a greatly increased level of intra- and interspecific competition, with an overall reduction in numbers. Whether this view is supported by available evidence is a matter of opinion, and we will return to it in the broader context of hedge survival in Chapter 6.

Invertebrates

Bearing in mind the diversity of hedgerow and verge vegetation, it is not surprising to find that this constitutes a vast reservoir of invertebrate life. Moreover, human interference in the form of cutting and spraying can bring about great changes in the diversity and composition of these animal populations in a minimum of time. It is at this level that the interests of man and nature tend to come into conflict. For instance, the stinging nettle (*Urtica dioica*), a frequent colonist of the inner zone of verges and the banks of hedgerows, is regarded by many as a pest and treated accordingly. Yet it is the food plant of the larvae of two of our most attractive butterflies, the peacock (*Inachis io*) and the small tortoiseshell (*Aglais urticae*). The wholesale extermination of nettles in recent years by sprays has undoubtedly contributed to the contraction of the range of these two species in some areas.

Verges and hedge banks support an array of small invertebrates, many of them arthropods, which either live below the soil surface, such as earthworms, or near it, like centipedes, millipedes and woodlice. Again, the species of flowering plants discussed in the previous chapter are each associated with a

85

range of predators, parasites and pollinators, the majority of which are insects, such as beetles (Coleoptera), aphids (Hemiptera), lacewings (Neuroptera) and flies (Diptera). Arachnids also abound, particularly spiders, all of which are carnivores, and mites, which play an important part as parasites in the formation of plant galls. In a short account it is impossible to do justice to all these groups, so the selection that follows has been made primarily on the basis of ecological interest and ease of study.

Insects

Carabid beetles (ground beetles)

The Caribidae are a large family of about 350 British species. They are known as ground beetles because most of their life is spent running about on the soil surface or just below it. They are mostly nocturnal, tending to hide by day under stones and among thick vegetation. Their principal colour is black and many have a characteristic metallic sheen. Some are quite large, their length ranging from 12 to 25 mm (½–1 in). Being carnivores, they are active in search of prey. This behaviour makes them particularly liable to capture in pitfall traps – containers such as jamjars or tins sunk in the ground and covered over lightly with vegetation such as grass or sticks (Fig. 4.5). Once captured, the beetles are unable to climb out and escape. This technique has been used to study the Carabids in a hedgerow at Ashton Wold, Northamptonshire.[33]

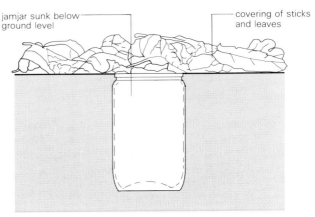

Figure 4.5   Pitfall trap constructed from a jamjar.

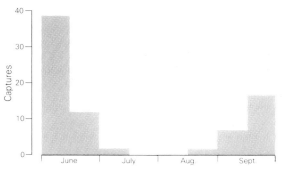

Figure 4.6   Seasonal fluctuations in captures of the beetle, *Nebria brevicollis.*[33]

Three species, *Trechus obtusus*, *Leistus ferrugineus* and *Abax parallelopipedus*, were found to be largely restricted to hedges, while three others, *Nebria brevicollis*, *Agonum dorsale* and *Bembidion guttula*, occurred both in hedgerows and outside them. Light was evidently an important factor influencing beetle distribution. Pitfall trapping served to reveal not only the range of movement but also seasonal fluctuations in distribution (Fig. 4.6). The peaks in June and September indicate that the beetle *Nebria brevicollis* was particularly active in the crop growing close to the hedge. At these seasons cover from the crop was either incomplete or absent while shelter from the adjacent hedge was most marked.

The studies of carabids do not appear to have included a system of marking, such as dots of quickly drying paint,[12] to study the pattern of movements of the beetle populations. Clearly, there are considerable possibilities here for further investigation of fluctuating numbers, movement patterns and the identity of individual populations.

Butterflies

Many species of butterflies are sporadic visitors to hedgerows and verges, and may even remain to breed there, but can hardly be said to form part of the resident insect community. A typical example is the brimstone (*Gonepteryx rhamni*) with its yellow males and greenish females, flying in May to June and again in August to September. Its distribution is determined by that of the food plant, buckthorn (*Rhamnus catharticus*), and, being a powerful flier, it ranges widely in woodland glades and other habitats. Again, the orange tip (*Anthocharis cardamines*) is a butterfly of spring (April), its larvae feeding on a variety of Crucifers such as cuckoo flower (*Cardamine pratensis*), a colonist of damp meadows, verges and hedge banks.

By contrast, the black hairstreak (*Strymonidia pruni*) is a woodland species also found in hedgerows, but it is now rare and extremely localised, being confined to a few localities in the Midlands, where its food plant sloe (*Prunus spinosa*) predominates.

The commonest colonists of hedges are all Satyrines (belonging to the family Satyridae – the 'browns'). Their larvae resemble one another in their behaviour in that they feed, mainly at night, on a range of common grasses. Most closely associated with the hedgerow shrub zone is the hedge brown or gatekeeper (*Pyronia tithonus*) (Fig. 4.7a), which can be observed flitting along the vegetation and visiting bramble flowers in July to August. Its populations, at least in the South of England, are subject to considerable fluctuations in numbers. Thus in 1984, the density in some localities in the West was so great that the insects spread onto the wider verges and into adjoining fields, overlapping the distribution of neighbouring butterfly species.

The grassland immediately adjoining hedges is occupied by another Satyrine, the ringlet (*Aphantopus hyperanthus*) (Fig. 4.7b), from which habitat it seldom strays far. Sometimes it can be observed flying up into the hedges and trees and mingling with the hedge browns, but it does not remain there for long. A third Satyrine species is the meadow brown (*Maniola jurtina*) (Fig. 4.7c), a butterfly whose life history and habits have been investigated more thoroughly than almost any other species.[34] This is an insect of open grassland, its main requirement being that the various grasses on which its larvae feed should remain relatively undisturbed throughout the year. Formerly, its distribution in well established fields was widespread but with the changes in farming practice to the ploughing and reseeding of leys roughly every four years, this is no longer so. No sooner has *Maniola* established itself in agricultural fields than they are ploughed once more and the populations destroyed. As a result, the butterfly now competes with the ringlet for verges and the belt of uncultivated vegetation between hedgerows and crops. As was explained earlier, under conditions of high population density and intraspecific competition, the hedge brown may also radiate into this zone.

Hedgerows are often extensions of woodland or at least closely associated with it. As conditions vary from brightly lit open spaces to deeper shade, the three species of Satyrines mentioned

Figure 4.7 Four butterflies closely associated with the hedgerow shrub zone but each having a distinct distribution: (a) hedge brown or gatekeeper (*Pyronia tithonus*); (b) ringlet (*Aphantopus hyperanthus*); (c) meadow brown (*Maniola jurtina*); (d) speckled wood (*Pararge aegeria*).

earlier are replaced by a fourth, the speckled wood (*Pararge aegeria*) (Fig. 4.7d), which is on the wing in April to May and again from July to September. Although common throughout Southern England and Wales, also in the Midlands, its distribution in the East of England is much more restricted and localised.

THE STUDY OF BUTTERFLY POPULATIONS

One of the great advantages of butterflies as subjects for observation is that, being relatively large, they are easy to identify and count. Moreover, they are readily marked either with dots of cellulose paint or by felt pens, so that studies of their movement and distribution can be made and their numbers estimated. The behaviour of Satyrines is particularly convenient for study since, once warmed up by an hour or so of sunshine, they remain on the wing for the rest of the day whether the sun is out or not. They even fly in the rain provided it is warm, and not too windy.

Under the auspices of the Institute of Terrestrial Ecology,

89

much has been done in recent years to devise standardised methods of conducting surveys by means of transects. Whether this is for the purpose of counting birds or butterflies, the principles are the same, namely that the procedure adopted must be systematic and repeatable.

Simple methods have been developed[35,36] for sampling populations and these work well in practice. The surveyor selects a route and counts all the butterflies seen while walking along it within an imaginary box 5 m ahead of him. The width of the box varies with the visibility and density of the species, from 6 m for widely ranging low-density species such as the small white (*Pieris rapae*), to 2 m for common high-density forms such as the hedge brown (*Pyronia tithonus*). To avoid large sampling errors, the length of the transect should be such as to include at least 40 individuals.

For comparative purposes, counts can be converted into a population index P given by

$$P = \frac{100NA}{L}$$

where L = length of the transect in metres (paces), N = number of butterflies recorded, and A = flight area obtained by multiplying L by the width of the habitat.

The hedge brown (*Pyronia tithonus*) is restricted in its distribution almost entirely to hedges, where it often occurs at a high density. Being easy to catch and mark, it provides ideal material for the estimation of population density by the process of mark–release–recapture. This depends upon the following principle: A sample of, say, 50 is captured, marked, released and allowed to randomise within the population. A further sample of, say, 45 is then taken. Suppose the second sample contains five individuals marked on the previous occasion, then the size of the flying population is approximately $(50 \times 45) \div 5 = 450$. In practice, at least a day should be allowed for randomisation between one sample and the next.

Bush crickets

Grasshoppers and crickets all belong to the same group of insects (order Orthoptera). They are easily recognised by their familiar shape, with much enlarged hind legs modified for jumping. When out of sight, they often advertise their presence by their familiar chirping (**stridulation**), caused by rubbing parts of the body together (the two wing cases in crickets).

True grasshoppers are not found in hedges but are insects of open grassland and heaths, but their near relatives, the bush crickets, occur commonly in hedgerows. One of the most abundant is the oak bush cricket (*Meconema thalassinum*), and, although it has a preference for oak trees, it is often common in hedges as well. It is about 15 mm long and coloured pale green, which provides it with good camouflage against the surrounding vegetation. Since it tends to inhabit the upper regions of hedges, it is best collected by beating the vegetation and spreading a sheet on the ground below. This technique is applicable to most of the less mobile invertebrates, particularly arthropods.

The remaining two species are the speckled bush cricket (*Leptophyes punctatissima*), recognisable by the absence of wings and a speckled body on a dark-green background, and the dark bush cricket (*Pholidoptera griseoaptera*), 14–15 mm long with a bright yellow underside. This is the only species with a pronounced song, which the male emits as a chirping from the depths of the vegetation particularly towards evening and at night during late summer, although it can also be heard sometimes by day.

Bush crickets are predominantly herbivores although they also take some animal food mainly in the form of small arthropods, particularly insects.

Spiders

Spiders, ticks and mites are all grouped together as the class Arachnida. They are sometimes confused with insects but one ready way of telling them apart is that, whereas insects all have three pairs of walking legs, arachnids have four pairs.

In late summer and autumn the gossamer festooning hedges in the early morning dew provides abundant evidence of spider activity. But even more striking can be the results of beating hedgerow vegetation in the manner referred to in the previous section. Sometimes it will be found that spiders outnumber all the other arthropods put together. Evidently, the hedge environment provides an abundant supply of food to be captured by spiders in their webs, mostly small winged insects such as flies and aphids.

One of the largest spiders found in hedges, although not commonly, is the garden spider (*Araneus diadematus*) with a distinctive white cross on its abdomen. Other close relatives are the small green *A. cucurbitus*, which frequently builds its web inside folded leaves, and *A. marmoreus pyramidatus*, which is characterised by a pale yellow body with a brown area at the hind end. Another relatively large species (about 6 mm long) is *Linyphia triangularis*, in which the female spins a dome-shaped web where she lurks hanging upside down.

Some of the most numerous spiders that will be represented in any sample obtained by beating are the money spiders, of which more than 250 species are found in Britain. They occur in a variety of colours and sizes; most are very small – about 2.5 mm long.

Another fascinating group are the largest spiders, typified by *Mitopus mario*, which differ from others in a number of respects, particularly the long slender legs on which they clamber about clumsily among the vegetation. Their ungainly mode of progression derives from the fact that they possess no silk glands and so are unable to spin a web. Like all spiders, they are carnivorous, feeding on small insects and other invertebrates and are mainly active at night.

Animal parasites and plant galls

A gall represents the response by a plant to attack by a wide variety of parasites ranging from bacteria and fungi to nematode worms, mites (arachnids) and insects of various kinds. They are formed either by the abnormal multiplication or the enlargement of the cells forming the plant's tissues. Either way, when fully formed, the structures produced are easily detectable with the naked eye by their shape, size and colours, and this makes their collection comparatively easy. Gall parasitism is quite common in hedgerows, the causes usually being either mites (Arachnida) or insects, the latter including midges (Diptera), wasps (Hymenoptera) and aphids (Hemiptera). Some common examples are summarised in Table 4.3. One of the most familiar is the robin's pincushion or moss gall due to the parasitic wasp, *Diplolepis rosae*, and conspicuous for its size and beautiful red colour in early September (Fig. 4.8).

The prelude to the stimulation of gall formation is invariably the laying of one or more eggs by a female in a plant's tissues. Just what stimulates abnormal development of the adjacent plant cells is uncertain – the oviposition of the female parasite or the presence of the egg, for example. But once the young larvae that hatch stop feeding, or when they pupate, or if they die, further development of the gall promptly ceases. Obtaining the parasites that hatch out from galls is a comparatively easy matter and this makes the subject an interesting one.

Figure 4.8   Robin's pincushion, a striking gall on dog rose caused by the parasitic wasp, *Diplolepis rosae.*

The galls are best kept in jars covered with fine mesh gauze (not plastic as this retains moisture). A layer of silver sand on the bottom of each jar will help to absorb excess moisture. One important precaution must be observed; the galls should not be removed from the parent plant until they have reached the fully developed stage, otherwise the parasites inside will die.

Sometimes the density of galls can be remarkable, as on oak leaves, which may each carry as many as 1200 silk button spangle galls caused by the wasp *Neuroterus numismatis.*

Many of these gall formers have complex life cycles involving an alternation of gall-forming and non-gall-forming generations. Further treatment of the subject is outside the scope of this book, but details are available in the excellent monograph by Arnold Darlington.[37]

Molluscs

Slugs and snails are often some of the commonest invertebrates occupying hedgerows, their populations reaching a high density. Their dependence on mucus (slime), both as a covering of the body surface and for the functioning of their lungs, explains their extreme sensitivity to the moisture of their environment. In dry weather and during the winter, the animals descend into the

Table 4.3 Some common galls on hedgerow shrubs and trees.

Species	Nature of gall	Cause
Shrubs		
hawthorn (*Crataegus* spp.)	at least three different galls caused by mites, aphids and midges, e.g.	mite (*Eriophyes goniothorax*)
hazel (*Corylus avellana*)	leaf-roll gall: leaf edges curl over forming a spike gall bud: resembles 'big bud' in blackcurrants (midsummer)	mite (*Eriophyes avellanae*)
dogwood (*Cornus sanguinea*)	pouch gall of leaf: resembles an inverted bottle; 8–10 mm (August–September)	midge (*Craneiobia corni*)
blackthorn (*Prunus spinosa*)	yellow–purple oval growths round edge of leaf; 3–5 mm (May–September)	mite (*Eriophyes similis*)
holly (*Ilex aquifolium*)	leaf miner: greenish white patterns (spring)	midge (*Phytomyza ilicis*)
wayfaring tree (*Viburnum lantana*)	pouch gall of leaf: usually near midrib; c.3 mm diameter; velvety green appearance (May–August)	mite (*Eriophyes viburni*)
rose (*Rosa* spp.)	robin's pincushion; moss gall (September)	wasp (*Diplolepis rosae*)
bramble (*Rubus* spp.)	rough swelling on one side of stem near tip (full size in September)	midge (*Lasioptera rubi*)

Trees		
field maple (*Acer campestre*)	leaf gall on upper leaf surface: globular or kidney-shaped; 3–6 mm; colour greenish orange–red–brown; situated in angle between primary and secondary vein (June–November)	mite (*Eriophyes macrochelus*)
sycamore (*A. pseudoplatanus*)		
ash (*Fraxinus excelsior*)	pod-like swelling on leaf midrib: length 25–50 mm; colour greenish light brown (June–September)	midge (*Dasyneura fraxini*)
oak (*Quercus* spp.)	at least 17 different galls all caused by gall wasps, e.g.	
	(i) oak apple: formed from a terminal or axillary bud; 25–40 mm (May–July)	wasp (*Biorhiza pallida*)
	(ii) spangle gall: often 100 or more on the underside of a leaf; flat, circular discs; 6 mm diameter, 2 mm thick; slightly hairy; at first yellowish green, later reddish (July–September)	wasp (*Neuroterus quercus-baccarum*)
English elm (*Ulmus procera*)	the leaf is converted into a pouch; outer surface at first grey, later red-purple (June–August)	aphid (*Schizoneura languinosa*)
crab apple (*Malus sylvestris*)	American blight (woolly aphis): infected branches develop knotty swellings; old growths sometimes become large	aphid (*Eriosoma lanigerum*)
wild cherry (*Prunus avium*)	apical bud infected giving distorted leaves with a reddish colour (June)	aphid (*Myzus cerasi*)
beech (*Fagus sylvatica*)	at least six different leaf galls all caused by mites; e.g.	mite (*Hartigiola annulipes*)
	pouch gall: develops into a yellowish cylinder on upper surface of leaf; 5 × 3 mm; starts yellow, finishes red-brown (July–September)	

deepest recesses of the vegetation where humidity is highest and where they are often extremely difficult to find. The best times to observe them are in the early morning before the dew has evaporated, and at dusk and after a rain storm, when they often swarm onto the surface of every kind of herbage. All land species are intolerant of low temperatures and the majority of those found in hedges hibernate during the winter, roughly from November to April, so observation must be confined to the summer months.

Most land molluscs require a supply of lime (calcium carbonate) in order to flourish. Snails need it to form their shells, but evidently there are other effects of a high pH that are not fully understood. Some species of snails can live in relatively lime-free conditions, such as heaths, but their populations are usually small and their shells relatively thin. Incidentally, the lack of lime does not seem to influence their maximum size to any great extent. Only a few species are true calcicoles and never occur in lime-free localities.

Woodlands are the richest of all mollusc habitats and, in lime-rich conditions, a single wood could be expected to yield at least 40 different species. This may well explain the diverse mollusc fauna occurring in many hedgerows, particularly those of woodland origin. The relationship existing between the mollusc communities of hedges and their age has been very little investigated. Several hedgerow species have been claimed to be indicators of woodland ancestry, such as the bulin (*Ena montana*), which is found occasionally in the South but is widespread in Europe, mostly in mountain habitats. However, such evidence as exists appears to be conflicting and this is an area that needs further investigation.

Their requirement for moisture helps to explain the preference of molluscs for the inner zone of verges and the lower zone of hedge banks where humidity tends to be high. But a habitat in the vicinity of a ditch is not without its dangers, for in winter the level of the water often rises half a metre or more and many hibernating snails are drowned. Where populations are at a high density, numerous shells of various species can often be found at the end of winter lying in ditches that are now dry. Most are undamaged, showing that death was due to causes other than predation.

Feeding and predation

Contrary to popular belief, most species of slugs and snails prefer to eat dead vegetation. In a hedgerow, mounds of rotting grass and other cut herbage provide particularly attractive feeding sites. However, that this generalisation is not invariable is demonstrated in Figure 2.12, for, in the absence of rotten material, fresh vegetation will always suffice. In this context, cultivated crops such as lettuces are particularly attractive.

Many species of slugs and snails will consume dead animal remains (carrion) but few are true carnivores. Some slugs such as *Testacella* eat earthworms, while the large black *Limax maximus*, although usually a herbivore, can become a rabid carnivore in captivity. Carnivorous snails are also rare exceptions, being confined to members of the families Zonitidae and Vitrinidae, which will eat other snails (particularly young animals) and their eggs.

Molluscs also provide important items of diet for many hedgerow vertebrates, notably mammals and birds. Rodents, particularly rats, are frequent predators on species such as the white-lipped snail (*Cepaea hortensis*), which they attack by nibbling round the lip of the shell. Where the level of bird predation is high, cracked shells of the garden snail (*Helix aspersa*), the white-lipped and brown-lipped snails (*Cepaea hortensis* and *C. nemoralis*) can often be found in large numbers near stones and in ditches, the snails having been attacked mainly by song thrushes. Unlike rodents, a bird holds a shell in its beak by the lip and cracks the spire open on a stone, making a series of clean

Figure 4.9 A typical thrush anvil stone with shells of the garden snail (*Helix aspersa*) and white-lipped snail (*Cepaea hortensis*).

breaks. Birds are creatures of habit and a single individual may use the same anvil stone on several occasions so that the accumulation of shells provides a measure of its diet (Fig. 4.9). A comparison of predated shells with those of populations living in the vicinity can be a useful means of assessing bird selectivity in terms of such variants as shell size and coloration.[25]

The shells of *Cepaea* vary in their background colour and degree of banding, and it is quite common for selection to occur in relation to these variants. Moreover, the advantage of a particular colour and pattern in achieving concealment may change with the time of year and the varying background. Sometimes, selection by birds may be in a particular direction (e.g. in favour of banded shells) irrespective of the fact that the variant in question is the rarer. Evidently, the bird somehow associates a particular appearance with food (**searching image**).[25]

Again, two neighbouring populations may differ in the distribution of a particular variant, such as banding, in the absence of any evidence of predation. This is known as an **area effect** and suggests either selective forces of an environmental kind or a degree of breeding isolation. Finally, it is worth remembering that a number of other variable species of snails occur frequently in hedgerows, such as the small *Discus rotundatus* whose distribution and predators have hardly been studied. These could well repay further exploration.

5

Motorway verges: unique environments

Most of our roads and tracks, and the verges associated with them, are at least 100 years old. Many are far older. By contrast, the motorways that now form an integral part of our environment are an innovation dating from the last 30 years or so. The first sections were, in fact, completed in 1959.

The design of motorways has evolved over the years since their beginning and has assumed varying forms in different parts of the country. The principal factors influencing their development will be discussed later. A generalised specification for a motorway was laid down in 1968 in a publication by the then Ministry of Transport entitled *Layout of Roads in Rural Areas.*[38] This envisaged two or three traffic lanes of width 3.7 m (12 ft) for each carriageway with a central reserve of 4 m (13 ft). On each side was a hard shoulder of 3.2 m (10 ft 6 in) bordered by a verge of 1.5 m (5 ft). The term 'verge' is not strictly appropriate here[39] as the land bordering motorways frequently merges into artificial cuttings or embankments that sometimes extend outwards for a considerable distance. However, for want of a better description, verge will be used throughout this chapter to define that portion of land bordering a motorway which lies between the hard shoulder and the boundary fence. It is usually grassed but may also be planted with a variety of shrubs and trees. A typical example from the M4 is shown in Figure 5.1.

The structure of motorways

Viewed from the air or on a map, the motorways of Britain radiate out ribbon-wise across the country, presenting a picture of relative simplicity and uniformity. In fact, their mode of design and that of their verges is frequently complex and highly variable.

99

Figure 5.1 A typical motorway verge (M4) colonised mainly by herbaceous vegetation. The young shrubs are hawthorn and the trees mainly sycamore and beech.

In selecting the course for a road, designers have to take into account several factors, such as its proximity to built-up areas and the need to sacrifice valuable agricultural land. The avoidance, where possible, of conservation areas, such as woodland and nature reserves, is also important. Major engineering projects like the construction of bridges can be expensive, so when planning a motorway the influence of topographical features must be borne in mind, such as the need to cross rivers and valleys, or to traverse steep hills. The geography of motorways varies greatly, but as a rough approximation about a third of the adjacent land is usually arable, a third grassland of other kinds and a third terrain of different sorts such as woodland or heath.

Geology and its significance

Just as the geology of an area determines its scenery, so, too, does it influence the character of a motorway. Rocks vary greatly in their hardness, durability and tendency to erosion, a fact that soon becomes apparent if we examine the slope of different roadside banks. The standard specification for an average verge gradient is 1 : 2, but this is only an approximation. Rocks such as chalk and limestone are relatively hard and stable, so in such areas the slope bordering a motorway can be increased. Clays and sandstones form lighter soils with a greater tendency to erosion by wind and rain, and where these border a roadway the incline may need to be more gradual in order to enable the roots of colonising plants to become established, binding the soil and forming a stable environment. Some rocks such as the metamorphic slates and shales found in parts of Wales and elsewhere are notoriously unstable and, if unchecked, are liable to cascade, causing dangerous obstructions to traffic. To safeguard such situations, it is sometimes necessary to erect strong iron barriers or even to cover parts of the verge area with heavy-duty metal netting.

A basic principle of motorway construction is that soil excavated from the bed of the road is dumped at the side forming the new verge. Where the superficial geological layer is quite thick and excavation is relatively shallow, the soil composing the verge will have much the same composition as that of the adjacent land. However, by the time it reaches its final position, much may have happened to it by way of drying, erosion and particularly compaction due to the passage of heavy machinery. As a result, its original physical properties, such as aeration and drainage, may have been greatly altered.

Sometimes, the quantities of excavated soil are insufficient for the construction of the necessary verges and considerable amounts may have to be introduced from elsewhere. For reasons of cost, it is obviously desirable that, whenever possible, these additional supplies should be obtained from sources nearby. Almost certainly, the geological properties of borrowed soil will differ from that already there, resulting in a patchwork effect that can change radically from one sector of roadway to another. On occasions, the introduction of foreign material can give rise to even greater discontinuity, as when colliery waste was used to fill in parts of the M62 in Yorkshire.

It is small wonder, then, that the plant communities colonising motorway verges can exhibit striking variations from one locality to another, presenting a scene of great ecological diversity.

Motorway vegetation

Driving along a motorway for any distance can be a somewhat monotonous undertaking. But the journey can be greatly enlivened by taking note of the frequent changes that occur in the surrounding environment. Indeed, it has even been seriously argued that the provision of diversity may be a significant factor in helping to keep sleepy drivers awake! Motorways in England and Wales seldom follow a single geological stratum for more than 40 km (25 miles) and changes often occur far more frequently.[39] These can have marked effects on the surrounding vegetation, which are easily discernible even from a distance.

Some of the most sensitive and easily observable indicators of environmental change are trees, and the frequency of occurrence of the different common species can provide an intriguing picture of the changing geology through which a motorway passes.

Suppose we were to follow the section of the M3 from London to Basingstoke. We begin on London Clay, which is neutral or slightly acid (pH around 6.5). Here the true vegetation is mixed deciduous, with a high proportion of oak. Next we pass to the sands of the Bagshot and Chertsey areas, where the pH (acidity) of the soil is in the region of 4.5, and we find a typical heathland community of calcifuge plants such as heathers, gorse and bracken. Predominant among the trees are birch and Scots pine. In the vicinity of Hook, the road crosses a short section of London Clay once more and the vegetation changes accordingly, but shortly afterwards it rises onto the Hampshire chalk. The pH of the soil is now 8.0 or higher, and the community of plants is typically calcicole. Oaks are scarce and are only able to colonise pockets of clay; the predominant trees are beech and ash. Thus in a distance of only 56 km (35 miles) the M3 passes through three quite distinct geological zones, each characterised by a different floral community.

The contrast between the adjacent plant populations and the species actually growing on motorway verges is sometimes striking. This is what we would expect. For whereas the flanking vegetation is natural in that it is the product of ecological processes often spanning many years, that of motorways, as we have seen, is all of recent origin and largely man-induced.

Motorway plants and their origins

In the construction of a motorway, the contractor is required to hand over the finished product with all the necessary seeding and planting completed. Thereafter, Local Authorities are responsible for the maintenance of the portions falling in their respective areas. Standard specifications require that the soil of verges should be appropriately prepared to the requisite depth and suitable fertilisers added before sowing. Clearly, it is import-

Table 5.1 A typical seed mixture for sowing motorway verges. The S values refer to specific cultivars.

Species	Proportion
perennial ryegrass (*Lolium perenne*) S23	6
red fescue (*Festuca rubra*) S59	2
smooth meadowgrass (*Poa pratensis*)	2
crested dog's tail (*Cynosurus cristatus*)	2
white clover (*Trifolium repens*) S100	1

ant that this should be done as soon as possible after the earthworks are completed in order to avoid surface soil losses due to erosion. A typical seed mixture containing several different grasses and clover is summarised in Table 5.1.

On occasions, the seeds of other species are included where environmental conditions are particularly suitable. Thus on the M2 south of the River Medway, and where the M4 crosses the Chiltern Hills, the geology is chalk and therefore particularly favourable to calcicole species. In both areas sainfoin (*Onobrychis viciifolia*) and salad burnet (*Sanguisorba minor*) have been successfully introduced, the former providing brilliant flashes of pink from June to September. Some species have proved particularly easy to introduce as seed and, once established, have proceeded to spread. Examples are gorse (*Ulex europaeus*) and broom (*Cytisus scoparius*), both typical colonists of heathland, which are now common on parts of the M1 in Bedfordshire, the M20 in Kent and on various sections of the M5 in the West Country.

The rate of sowing varies with the gradient of the bank: the greater the slope, the higher the concentration of seed required. Where the terrain is particularly difficult, such as on steep slopes and where soil conditions are poor, a process of hydro-seeding may be employed. This consists of spraying the ground with a mixture of seeds, organic mulch and sometimes fertilisers using a hydraulic pump. Since all the essential ingredients for germination and growth are provided, the seeds are able to become established without having to rely on the inadequate supply of nutrients in the surrounding medium.

In addition to the seeding of verges, the Department of the Environment (formerly the Ministry of Transport) has embarked upon an extensive programme of planting trees, aided by technical help from the Forestry Commission. Some idea of the magnitude of the operation can be gained from the fact that, on occasions, the planting programme has exceeded 1½ million trees in a year. In selecting suitable species and siting areas for planting, particular attention is paid to the need for hiding unsightly objects, softening the hard outlines of structures such as bridges and conforming to the outlines of the existing topography. It is said that shrubs and trees by roadsides help to deaden the noise of traffic, so their planting can have particular significance in the vicinity of built-up areas.

Among the most popular trees for roadside planting are field maple (*Acer campestre*), sycamore (*Acer pseudoplatanus*) silver birch (*Betula pendula*), Scot's pine (*Pinus sylvestris*), oak (*Quercus robur*), beech (*Fagus sylvatica*) and ash (*Fraxinus excelsior*). Smaller trees and shrubs include hazel (*Corylus avellana*), goat willow (*Salix caprea*), hawthorn (*Crataegus monogyna*), blackthorn (*Prunus spinosa*) and elder (*Sambucus nigra*).

By comparison with herbaceous plants, trees and shrubs grow comparatively slowly and therefore represent more long-term investments. It will be several generations before the planting schemes of the last 20 years or so reach full maturity, by which time many of the forest trees planted among the smaller species will have dominated them and reduced them to obscurity.

Invasions from outside

The vegetation of a motorway verge derived from initial seeding is unlikely to remain unchanged for long. The extent and rate of penetration by other plant species depends upon a number of factors, such as the nature of the terrain, seeds already present in the topsoil, the arrival of seeds and spores from elsewhere and methods of management, such as the frequency of cutting and the application of selective herbicides. The greatest source of new colonists is the adjoining land and, if this is cultivated, it will almost certainly be a reservoir of some of the common weeds. Many of these are annuals, such as groundsel (*Senecio vulgaris*), shepherd's purse (*Capsella bursa-pastoris*) and wild oat (*Avena fatua*). In competition with the more strongly growing herbaceous perennials, they seldom survive for long. These include pernicious weeds listed in the Weeds Act of 1959, such as spear thistle (*Cirsium vulgare*), creeping thistle (*C. arvense*), curled dock (*Rumex crispus*), broad-leaved dock (*R. obtusifolius*) and ragwort (*Senecio jacobaea*). Since the Department of the Environment requires that its agent Local Authorities should take steps to prevent the seeding of such weeds if landowners

Table 5.2 Commonest wild herbaceous plants on the M62 motorway from Liverpool to Manchester in order of their apparent obviousness.[40]

common couch	(*Elymus repens*)
creeping thistle	(*Cirsium arvense*)
spear thistle	(*C. vulgare*)
broad-leaved dock	(*Rumex obtusifolius*)
cocksfoot	(*Dactylis glomerata*)
stinging nettle	(*Urtica dioica*)
lesser burdock	(*Arctium minus*)
mugwort	(*Artemisia vulgaris*)
cow parsley	(*Anthriscus sylvestris*)
hogweed	(*Heracleum sphondylium*)
hard rush	(*Juncus inflexus*)
coltsfoot	(*Tussilago farfara*)
common sorrel	(*Rumex acetosa*)
meadow vetchling	(*Lathyrus pratensis*)

complain, it may be necessary to apply appropriate methods of control – usually selective herbicides.

Clearly, the rate, extent and diversity of the colonisation of motorway verges from outside will vary greatly from one area to another depending on the kinds of ecological factors outlined above. A typical example has been recorded[40] on the 30 miles of the M62 motorway between Liverpool and Manchester, which crosses a relatively uniform area of Triassic Sandstone. The commonest herbaceous species observed are summarised in order of their obviousness in Table 5.2.

At present our knowledge of changes in the vegetation of our motorway verges is only fragmentary and we are still far from discerning any overall patterns of variation. In addition to more extensive studies, which are badly needed, we also need a more consistent regime of management so that ecological changes due to fluctuations in human influence can be reduced in future to a minimum.

Animal populations

If our knowledge of the vegetation of motorway verges is deficient, that of the build-up of animal populations is even more fragmentary. One of the peculiarities of motorways, as we have seen (p. 104), is that the ecological environment never remains the same for long stretches. Changes due to such variations as the underlying geology and fluctuations in managerial procedures combine to produce a patchwork of ecological islands. In such circumstances, ecosystems tend to develop in a haphazard manner so that the niches present in one area may differ substantially from those in another adjacent to it. One outcome of such a distributional pattern is that a particular species may achieve abundance in one locality but be almost absent from another, depending on the varying physical conditions and the density of predators and parasites.

Little is known about populations of mammals inhabiting the verges of motorways. From time to time badgers are reported as being run over on the highway at night, but it seems likely that these will have been based in adjacent woodland rather than among the motorway vegetation. A few studies have been carried out on the populations of small mammals along major roadways in North America.[41] These have involved extensive trapping and marking for the purpose of estimating the density and mobility of different species. Since the majority of these do not occur in Britain and the roadside environments of the USA and Canada differ substantially from our own, any findings from such investigations are likely to be of little relevance to our situation.

Among birds, we cannot but be struck by the frequent occurrence of birds of prey, particularly kestrels (*Falco tinnunculus*), hovering in the vicinity of roadside verges. They are now common on parts of the M5 in the West, indicating that here ecosystems have built up to the extent of supporting populations of small mammals. But whether these are located in the verges themselves or on the land nearby remains open to question. One group of birds directly involved in changing the ecology of motorways are the finches, particularly the greenfinch (*Carduelis chloris*). This is a berry eater and an effective disperser of the seeds that pass through the animal's gut unharmed. It has undoubtedly played a major part in promoting the spread of hawthorn, which has characterised sections of several motorways such as the M4.

Insect populations lend themselves particularly well to study since they are relatively easy to observe and sample, so it is not surprising to find that they have come in for more attention. Incidentally, they illustrate well the discontinuity of motorway ecology, attaining large numbers in some areas while remaining almost absent from localities nearby. Some notable studies have been made recently[42] of certain Continental motorways where conditions are somewhat similar to our own. In an area near Basle (Switzerland), hawthorn bushes growing on the central reservation and on verges are frequently infested by the green apple aphid (*Aphis pomi*), resembling our greenfly, from May to July. When the population density was high in some places, the insect was found to be almost absent not far away. Evidently, such situations are not peculiar to the Basle district but are widespread in other parts of Switzerland and in France. The influence of natural predators was tested experimentally by setting up groups of potted hawthorn bushes beside the carriageways. Some were enclosed (controls) and others exposed to the outside, giving access to predators (mostly various other insects). In general, the level of predation was lower than might have been expected, and it is clear that the control of these insect populations is a complex affair involving both physical and biotic factors. Some of the most significant factors would appear to be the following:

(a) The activities of predators, but at a relatively low level.
(b) Biochemical changes in the host plants resulting from the accumulation of high quantities of amino acids as a result of the emissions from car exhausts (see also p. 108). These would favour the growth of plants and hence of the insects feeding on them.
(c) The microclimate of motorway verges, which may be particularly favourable to insect multiplication. On warm days in some places the average temperature beside a carriageway was found to be 1–3°C higher than elsewhere.

In Britain, various similar outbreaks in insect numbers have been reported from time to time. For instance, in 1978 and 1979, densities of the grasshopper *Chorthippus brunneus* were particularly high on parts of the central reserve of the A423(M) and M4 compared with sites nearby. Attempts have been made to assess the reasons for outbreaks in populations of the buff tip moth (*Phalera bucephala*) and the goldtail moth (*Euproctis similis*) on the A423(M) and M63 respectively.[43] Again, they indicate that variations in numbers cannot be attributed to a single cause but probably result from the interaction of a number of different factors. As was suggested in the Basle study, one of the more significant could be the build-up of nitrogenous material derived from car exhausts (if, indeed, this occurs (p. 109)), particularly amino acids that promote the growth of plants and their associated insect herbivores, both larvae and adults.

In the future, the nature of animal populations outside motorways and their increase or demise will depend to a large extent on the kinds of management regimes adopted and their consistency. Continuous stretches of vegetation treated in a uniform manner could provide important future reservoirs for wildlife. The key to such development lies in the diversity of herbs, shrubs and trees, and hence the range of ecological niches that they can provide. That this may be happening to a limited extent already is suggested by the increasing number of larger vertebrates such as hawks now in evidence. Devising a coherent management programme to meet the diverse conditions beside motorways will not be easy, but even the limited evidence outlined above suggests that the outcome in terms of wildlife promotion could amply repay any trouble and expense involved.

Pollution and its effects

Bearing in mind the volume of traffic, it is hardly surprising that pollution, mostly with the by-products of internal combustion engines, reaches a higher level on motorways than on any other thoroughfares in Britain. The main pollutants can be classified as follows:[44]

(a) Gases emitted by vehicle exhausts, which consist largely of the oxides of carbon, nitrogen and sulphur, and volatile fractions of unburnt fuels.
(b) Minute particles of various sorts, particularly carbon (in smoke) and oil droplets.
(c) Larger particles including oil, rubber and dust from the road surface, and also corroded fragments from passing vehicles (e.g. rust). These are dispersed by the wind or washed by the rain onto the soil and vegetation within a zone of approximately 2.5 m (c. 3 yards) from the hard shoulder.
(d) Lead compounds derived from anti-knock additives to petrol, which are dispersed both as particles and in volatile form.
(e) Salt added to the carriageways during freezing weather and retained to varying extents at the roadside for the rest of the year.

Within this miscellaneous collection of items, present evidence suggests that the oxides of nitrogen, lead compounds and salt are the most significant in their influence on the environment and wildlife. The account that follows will therefore be confined to them. At the outset it must be stressed, however, that the full effects of even these relatively well documented substances are still far from being fully understood.

108

Oxides of nitrogen

Atmospheric pollution with the oxides of nitrogen consists of the gases nitric oxide (NO) and nitrogen dioxide (NO_2) in varying proportions. Since the two usually occur together as a mixture, a convenient shorthand often employed is NO_x. In urban areas the concentration of NO_x can vary from 0.08 ppm (Reading) to 0.55 ppm (Leicester).[45] In rural areas, the concentration is a good deal lower.

It is widely held that the presence of oxides of nitrogen in the air can be beneficial to the biochemistry of plants in accelerating the synthesis of amino acids and hence promoting growth.[42,43] However, under experimental conditions, it is found that the reactions of different species to concentrations of NO_x vary greatly. For some the gases may be a benefit; for others they are a poison. An important additional dimension to the discussion[45] is that NO_x pollution by roadsides is usually accompanied by other gases, particularly sulphur dioxide (SO_2). There is evidence that, when the two gases occur together, their deleterious effects are additive, but since this is a finding that has yet to be tested in the field, we know virtually nothing of their effects on motorway verge vegetation. At present, therefore, the ecological roles of NO_x and SO_2 remain uncertain. They are undoubtedly harmful in some circumstances but could be beneficial in others when the concentration of SO_2 is low and NO_x is exerting a predominant effect in promoting the formation of nitrogenous compounds such as amino acids.

Compounds of lead

The amount of lead added to petrol annually in Britain as tetraalkyl lead fluid is of the order of 9000 tonnes. Of this some 60–70 per cent is emitted by car exhausts into the atmosphere, a significant proportion being deposited on motorway verges.[46] The majority of lead pollution is concentrated within a zone of some 50 m (55 yards) on either side of the roadway; only 10–30 per cent of the total extends outwards as far as 100 m. The amount of lead deposited depends considerably on the nature of the surface. For instance, it has been estimated that the rate of deposition on grass is about four times that on bare soil. Similarly, the rough or hairy surfaces of plants accumulate lead at approximately 10 times the rate of smooth leaves. Again, different roadside vegetation intercepts lead compounds with varying degrees of efficiency; the rate of accumulation in soil under trees may be as much as twice that under grass in the open.[46]

The lead emitted by car exhausts is a complex mixture of compounds, but the principal one found on the soil and vegetation bordering carriageways is lead sulphate ($PbSO_4$). Beside rural roads the concentration can be quite low (<10µg/g dry weight) but at 30 m (33 yards) from a busy motorway it can rise to 10 times this amount or more.

As for the influence of lead on plants, extensive research has shown it to be deleterious, although the magnitude of its effects varies greatly from one species to another. High concentrations in the soil tend to produce a more adverse response than comparable deposits on plant leaves, indicating that lead is assimilated into the tissues mainly via the roots. Curiously, where lead-susceptible plants have been grown on polluted motorway verges, although there was a considerable uptake of the metal in the roots, comparatively little was transferred to the shoots. It now seems certain that the main effects of lead on plants is to inhibit the growth of roots and shoots. Additional effects may be an imbalance in mineral nutrition and a reduction in the rates of photosynthesis and respiration, although these are less well established. The fact is that, while ecological effects of lead contamination undoutedly exist, we are still far from understanding fully the ways by which they come about.

REACTIONS BY PLANTS TO LEAD POLLUTION

Although we may be unclear regarding the physiological and ecological effects of lead compounds on plants, thanks to the work carried out mainly at Liverpool University,[47] we know a good deal more about the capabilities of different species to adjust to polluted conditions. It has long been known that, in the vicinity of lead mines, while certain species of plants are able to tolerate the contaminated soil, others cannot. Moreover, there is extensive evidence that most, if not all, pollution-tolerant populations, have achieved their adaptation through the evolution of strains with a specific tolerance of lead. Incidentally, a similar evolutionary process has occurred in response to other heavy-metal contaminants such as copper and zinc. It is an odd fact that some species, such as the ribwort plantain (*Plantago lanceolata*), are able to develop lead resistance while others apparently are not. The common roadside grass, red fescue (*Festuca rubra*), also possesses the ability to evolve tolerance, and since its distribution is widespread it should provide a useful indicator of pollution. This idea has been put to the test.[47]

Samples of red fescue plants were collected from three different localities:

(a) the soil tips of the Trelogan lead mines, an area of high contamination;
(b) a section of the M6 motorway known to be moderately polluted, at distances of 0 (adjacent to the hard shoulder; control), 1, 3, 7 and 13 m from the hard shoulder; and
(c) Penn Common, a relatively uncontaminated area of rough grassland more than 200 m (220 yards) from the nearest road.

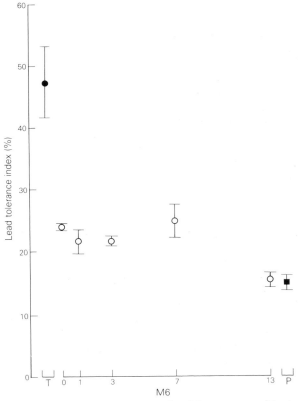

Figure 5.2 Lead tolerance indices of red fescue grass (*Festuca rubra*) from three localities (mean of five plants per locality ± standard error):[47] ●, Trelogan lead mine (T); ○, sites of M6 motorway verge (the number is the distance in metres from the motorway hard shoulder); ■, uncontaminated site at Penn Common (P).

Tolerance indices were determined for the various groups of plants by measuring the extent of root formation when grown in lead-contaminated and uncontaminated growth media under carefully controlled conditions. The results are summarised in Figure 5.2.

As we would expect, plants from the lead mine area proved to be much more lead-tolerant than those from the rough grassland (by a factor of about 3). The tolerance of M6 individuals within 7 m of the hard shoulder was approximately half that of plants from the lead mine and greater than those from the 13 m zone. It was also greater than plants from the control area adjacent to the hard shoulder, although the difference was not statistically significant.

The degrees of lead tolerance evolved in the three sites appear to be related to the concentrations of exchangeable lead present in the soil, that is to say, the amount of free lead available for uptake by the plant roots (Table 5.3). Reference to Table 5.3 shows that, within the zone of the M6 verge, the red fescue had evolved lead tolerance in response to a wide range of contamination. For instance, the mean tolerance of plants at 7 m from the hard shoulder was not significantly different from that at the edge. This suggests a high level of sensitivity by *Festuca rubra* to small quantities of contaminants. The results of previous research have suggested that the amounts of lead occurring at 7 m from the edge of the M6 would be unlikely to be toxic. But the evolution of lead-tolerant strains in this region suggests strongly that such levels do, indeed, damage non-tolerant individuals. Since the levels of lead contamination in the soil of the M6 verges are comparable with those of other motorways in Britain, it seems likely that the toxic effects of exhaust-emitted lead compounds may be much more widespread than had previously been supposed.

Table 5.3 Exchangeable lead concentrations in the soil (0–5 cm depth) of three sites colonised by red fescue (*Festuca rubra*).[47]

Site	Lead concentration (mg/g dry weight)
Treloggan	804.32
M6 (0 m)	345.66
M6 (1 m)	101.37
M6 (3 m)	52.12
M6 (7 m)	0.85
M6 (13 m)	–
Penn Common	–

De-icing salt

It has been estimated that about 1½ million tonnes of common salt (NaCl) are applied as a de-icing agent to the highways of Britain every year. As far as motorways are concerned, the rate varies enormously depending largely on the weather. In a warm winter, salt application can be of the order of 5.4 tonnes per lane kilometre, while in severe conditions it can reach double that amount or more.[48] Mention was made earlier (p. 49) of the physical and chemical effects of sodium ions on soil. In moderation, they can improve the crumb structure by causing the clay particles to clump together, thereby increasing aeration and drainage. However, in excess, the process of flocculation is upset, the crumb structure breaks down and any clay present becomes compacted in an impermeable layer. High concentrations of sodium and chloride ions can also be lethal to many roadside plants.

One of the principal dangers to verge vegetation from salting derives from the fact that, once applied, a residue of salt can remain in the soil for a considerable period. Thus, samples of soil taken from nine different sections of motorway central reserves covering every month for three years showed that variations in sodium concentration from month to month could be enormous.[48] In general, there was a tendency for levels to increase in March and April and thereafter to decline throughout the summer until the lowest concentrations were reached in October. Since summer rainfall tends usually to be exceeded by evaporation, little removal of sodium would be expected and there was a slowing up during dry periods. As predicted, salt pollution proved to be higher on central reservations than on verges. At roadsides it extended to about 2 m (2 yards) from the hard shoulder, thereafter declining rapidly. It is in this zone that plants are most at risk.

The pattern of salt use varies from one part of the country to another, but everywhere the factors affecting it are the same. This has enabled a mathematical model to be derived so that, for a given site, using estimates of rainfall, evaporation and rates of salt application, the expected sodium residue can be calculated. The predicted values are found to agree quite closely with those actually observed. The model has proved useful not only in predicting surface concentrations but in simulating the distribution of sodium and chloride ions down to a depth of 50 cm (about 20 in).[48]

The damage inflicted by salt on vegetation at the fringe of

113

verges is relatively unimportant. Bare patches of ground beside the hard shoulder may look unsightly for a time but in the course of the summer they are usually recolonised by plants of some kind. More significant are the effects of salt sprayed by vehicles onto nearby trees and shrubs. Here there is much circumstantial evidence but little objective information. Experiments involving the spraying of salt solution at different concentrations onto container-grown plants[48] have enabled indices of tolerance to be worked out (100 per cent = total tolerance). From these it is clear that pollution of the soil is much more damaging than that of the aerial parts. Thus, for a selection of 11 common species, tolerance of salt spray of the stems and leaves ranged from 100 to 91 per cent. For the same species, tolerance of soil contamination varied from 100 per cent in grey willow (*Salix cinerea*) and sea buckthorn (*Hippophae rhamnoides*), to 62 per cent for goat willow (*Salix caprea*) and 61 per cent for hawthorn (*Crataegus monogyna*).

COLONISATION BY HALOPHYTIC PLANTS

While the salting of motorways may have its disadvantages for most plants growing on the edge of verges, it also confers unexpected benefits on others. As we have seen, saline conditions in the soil may persist throughout the year and this has permitted colonisation by an assortment of species usually confined to estuarine conditions. All have a high salt tolerance and hence are known as *halophytes*. Their arrival has been particularly noticeable alongside motorways such as the M1, M2 and M20, which carry a high volume of holiday traffic during the summer, thus providing a potential means of seed dispersal on the mud of tyres, mudguards and elsewhere on the bodies of cars. The list of arrivals is now considerable and includes such well known salt-loving species as the sea plantain (*Plantago maritima*), sea spurrey (*Spergularia marina*), sand spurrey (*S. rubra*) and sea aster (*Aster tripolium*), to mention only a few.

One of the most successful and widespread maritime colonists has been the reflexed meadow-grass (*Puccinellia distans*), whose distribution has been investigated in some detail.[19] Its rapid spread along verges can be explained by reference to its usual habitats, which tend to be on the edge of saltmarshes, often on disturbed, compacted and poorly drained soils – conditions similar to those obtaining at the side of many motorways. Moreover, the plant produces large numbers of small, light seeds that are well adapted for adhering to mud and for dispersal in the slipstream of vehicles.

Like other halophytes, the arrival of *Puccinellia* is invariably preceded by extensive salting, which often destroys the resident verge plants, leaving bare patches of ground (sometimes referred to as 'salt burn'). It is in these open areas devoid of other competitors that colonisation by maritime species has been particularly successful. *Puccinellia* now occurs beside major roads throughout much of Northern, Central and Eastern England (Fig. 5.3). As will be seen from the map, it has colonised areas of the A1, M1, M42, M46 and M62, forming more or less continuous populations. Others such as those from the area of the Mersey (M52), Norfolk (A149), Kent (M2 and M26) and Surrey (A24) are at present more or less discrete entities.

Of all the halophytes colonising motorway verges, *Puccinellia*

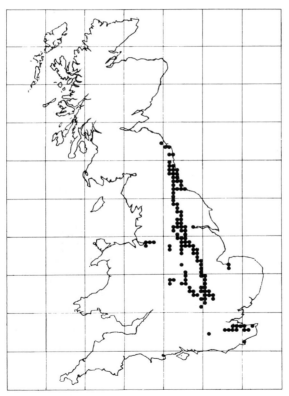

Figure 5.3 Distribution of the reflexed meadowgrass (*Puccinellia distans*) by roadsides in Britain.[19]

seems to be spreading the most rapidly, but the rate varies some-what from one area to another. In the North and Northeast it has been particularly successful, owing to the extensive areas of salt burn alongside such roads as the M1, M56 and M62. In the South, however, salt burn is less extensive, and in Bedfordshire and Kent maritime species are found competing with normal verge plants, creating isolated populations. The overall distribution pattern thus appears to be a function of the amount of salt-ing, which is considerably higher in the North than in the South.

Finally, we may well ask how halophytes like *Puccinellia* reached the motorways in the first place. Reference to Figure 5.3 shows that they can mostly be traced along major roads running to within about 10 km (6 miles) of coastal sites providing access for vehicles. Thus, populations on the A1, M1 and M62 could have come from Holy Island (Northumberland). Similarly, populations in Kent along the A2, M2 and M20 have a direct con-nection with the Isle of Sheppey. Alternatively, it is likely that some areas inland were colonised from others nearby, an example being Streetly quarry (Nottinghamshire), which is near the M1 and M62, both of which are used for the transport of stone from the quarry.[19]

An alternative explanation of the distribution of species such as *Puccinellia* could be that their seeds were present as a conta-minant in the mixture used for planting the verges when they were originally constructed. Enquiries of the official seed testing station and major seed importers, however, have provided no clear evidence of maritime species being introduced in this way. So we are left with the overwhelming conclusion that the intro-duction of halophytes to our motorways has been predominantly from local sources, and that the principal agent responsible for their dispersal and subsequent distribution has been man.

6

Hedgerows under threat

For the ever increasing number of people who are aware of it, the rural countryside of Britain presents a fair and pleasant scene. It is also admired by much of the rest of the world. Within this panorama, hedgerows and the verges associated with them form an essential part. As we have seen in the previous chapters, our environment, as we know it today, is far from being just a gift of nature. It is sometimes customary to describe areas such as chalk downs and heathland as natural, implying that they have always been here. But this is to misrepresent the real situation.

Before the coming of man, much of Britain was covered with primeval forest, and the ecological conditions existing now are the outcome of subtle interactions over many centuries between the activities of human beings and the forces of nature. The advent of hedgerows and verges provides a typical example of such interaction. Their pattern today represents a response to distinct needs – to mark the boundaries of property and to prevent livestock from straying. Two processes have largely determined their pattern and extent: the enclosure of land, particularly during the period 1750–1850, and changes in agricultural practice resulting from a fluctuating economic situation.

Over the last 25 years or so, the agricultural scene has changed more rapidly than ever before due largely to a new set of economic forces, among them an urge by government towards increased productivity and advances in every field of husbandry. A continual rise in the cost of labour has resulted in a smaller workforce and, concurrently, the introduction of intensive methods based on an industrial approach. Modern farm machinery is large and economical, provided it is used correctly. But for its effective deployment, fields must be of sufficient size. When hedgerows have stood in the way of expansion, they have been grubbed up. It is sometimes claimed that hedge destruction

117

is a feature only of recent years but this is an oversimplification. With the continual expansion of arable farming since the collapse of the wool trade in the late 18th century and the rise of the industrial areas, hedge removal has been going on intermittently for the last 200 years. But recently the pace has accelerated dramatically. Estimates of the extent of destruction vary, but it is probably true to say that about a fifth of Britain's 800 000 km (500 000 miles) of hedgerows have been removed in the last 40 years. During the period of maximum activity between 1946 and 1974, it has been estimated that some 230 000 km (140 000 miles) of hedges disappeared.[21,49]

It would be wrong to lay responsibility for this massive destruction solely at the door of the farmers; an appreciable proportion has been non-agricultural. In the period 1925–39 urban encroachment on farmland is estimated to have accounted for the loss of around 1600 km (1000 miles) of hedges a year. In the post-war period it has dropped somewhat to about 1100 km (700 miles), but this does not include the effects of projects such as the construction of motorways and airfields, and the extension of opencast mining operations. Setting the situation in broad perspective, it has been calculated[21] that, since the last war, a total of 32 000 km (20 000 miles) of hedges have been lost for non-agricultural reasons compared with 192 000 km (120 000 miles) removed by farmers.

Although the reasons for hedge removal for agriculture have not varied, the rate and extent of the process has fluctuated in different parts of the country, depending on the topography of the land, the nature of the crops and local agricultural practice. In flat open areas, such as East Anglia, elimination has been high, while in more enclosed regions, such as the West Country (particularly Devon), with its extensive systems of small fields, it has been considerably lower. However, everywhere the rate of removal has far exceeded that of replacement. In this connection it is worth remembering that, whereas modern machinery can grub up a hedge in an hour or less, it takes 20 years or more to grow an effective new one.

Hedgerows and conservation

Over the last 25 years or so, the standard of living in Britain has gradually risen, until today we have a more affluent society with greater opportunities for leisure and vastly increased mobility. Interest in agricultural land is no longer confined to the farmer, but it is widely regarded by the public as an amenity held in trust by the farming community for the nation as a whole.

In Britain, the amenity movement has assumed two forms, the protection of our characteristic landscape and the preservation of its flora and fauna.[22] The two are clearly related, but nonetheless a curious dichotomy exists between them. This is illustrated by the fact that they are the respective responsibility of two quite separate government agencies, the Countryside Commission with the terrain and the Nature Conservancy Council with wildlife. In the past, activities of the two bodies have been by no means always in accord but, increasingly, attempts are being made to bring the two viewpoints closer together.

Looking to the future, we need to ask ourselves four key questions:

(a) Is further removal of hedges inevitable? Indeed, is it possible that we could eventually witness their total destruction?

(b) Would their further removal destroy the countryside? What criteria should we use in judging 'destruction'?

(c) If the answer to (b) is 'Yes', what measures could be taken to prevent further destruction?

(d) Is an alternative strategy possible which allows the farmer to make full use of modern developments while conserving and, if possible, improving the countryside and its wildlife?

Before we can answer these questions, it will be desirable to do two things. First we need to examine a little more closely the intimate structure of hedges and the populations they support in order to see more clearly what is really involved in their destruction. Secondly, we need to draw up an inventory of the supposed disadvantages and advantages of hedgerows and verges. Some of these have been considered in other contexts in previous chapters, but we now need to draw them closer together.[50]

Hedgerows and verges as ecosystems

In the previous chapters we have been concerned with plants and animals separately, and this approach has had its merits in serving to highlight interesting species in relation to their distribution and mode of life. But individual organisms never exist alone; they live in varying degrees of competition and collaboration with others, so the destruction of a habitat such as a hedge involves not only the removal of individual species but of all the others on which they depend.

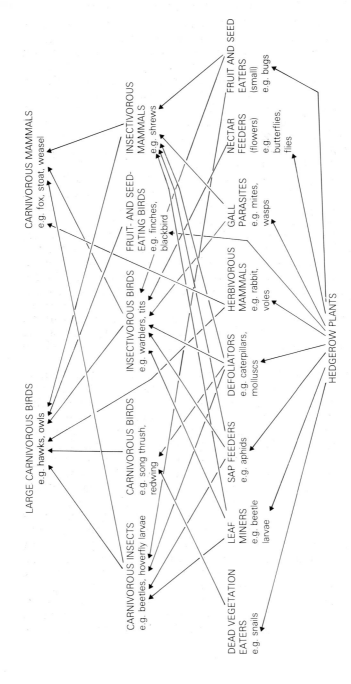

Figure 6.1 Some ecological niches and food relationships in hedgerows. Arrows indicate the direction of flow of resources.

As we saw in Chapter 4, hedges and verges support a large assortment of animals. These in turn depend upon a diversity of plants, the ultimate assimilators of energy. Such an arrangement, in which a number of units are linked together and mutually dependent, is known as a **system**. Since the linkages here are ecological, we can refer to the whole as an **ecosystem**, part of which is depicted in Figure 6.1. The arrows joining the different levels of the ecosystem (**trophic levels**) represent the passage of resources in the form of food such as energy and essential minerals. The complete set of criss-cross relationships covering part or whole of the system is known as a **food web**.

As the ecologist Elton pointed out many years ago,[51] when analysing the food relationships within an ecosystem, it is often useful, particularly among animals, to take into account the economic positions of the organism. Thus, referring to Figure 6.1, among the insects there are leaf miners, defoliators, gall formers, and nectar, fruit and seed eaters. Each of these is referred to as the organism's **ecological niche** within the community where it occurs. Among its other uses, the niche concept can be valuable in enabling a prediction to be made regarding the likelihood that a particular species will occur in a specific locality. Conversely, should the essential components of a niche disappear, as all too often happens under man's influence, it will be unlikely that the various species concerned will survive unless they are able to adjust their mode of life to the changed conditions.

It has been claimed that hedgerows help to provide an optimal balance between certain human activities and the natural environment, but concrete evidence to support or refute such a statement is difficult, if not impossible, to obtain. The reasons for this are not far to seek. Hedgerows and verges are of highly variable composition, and occur in a great variety of ecological contexts. All are subject to the processes of competition and change, but these assume different forms from one place to another. Thus a species of plant or animal may be abundant and regarded as a pest in one area while its influence is insignificant in another. Again, hedges frequently border fields containing monocrops (crops of a single kind), and here the ecological relationships between the two will depend partly on the locality and partly upon the sort of crop being grown. But in spite of these limitations, it is nonetheless possible to take a rather more objective view of the ecological relationships of hedgerows and verges.

Among the herbivorous mammals occupying hedgerows, the various species of voles (Fig. 4.1) can be some of the most troublesome to farmers. Their population numbers are subject to large fluctuations, and at their maximum density they can reach pest proportions, devouring any green material within their range, particularly the young shoots of crop plants. Reference to Figure 6.1 will show that their predators are the larger carnivorous birds, such as owls, and also mammals such as the fox, stoat and weasel. Observations based on the food remains regurgitated by owls (owl pellets) and the food caches of mammals have shown that their toll of the local vole populations is certainly high, and it is claimed that, when such conditions prevail, crop damage by voles is kept to a minimum. Where hedges have been removed and the animals have colonised the fields, the results on occasions have been devastating.

To survive and breed, birds of prey need trees as a refuge, some preferably with hollow trunks for nesting. They are frequently found in hedges, marginal land and small areas of woodland, which often border agricultural fields. These are, however, potential sources of timber and all too readily subject to felling and removal, with serious consequences for the bird population. Similarly, carnivorous mammals such as the fox inhabit hedge banks, while stoats and weasels rely on dense hedgerow vegetation for refuge and hunting grounds. Removal of hedges can mean the end of these populations and a consequent relaxing of predation pressure on their prey.

At a lower level of the food web, the range of habitats occupied by insects is enormous, and these often support dense populations of insectivores, particularly birds. One of the great dangers of monocrops, on which much of the world's food supply depends, is that an unaccustomed disease to which no adequate chemical control exists, could sweep rapidly through a particular crop such as wheat with catastrophic consequences. It is therefore vitally important that, wherever possible, chemical control of pests should be reinforced by biological control based on natural predator–prey relationships.

Supposed disadvantages of hedgerows

Hedges restrict the use of large machines

The advantages to the arable farmer of enlarging fields by the removal of hedges where necessary have been studied in some detail at Cambridge.[52] One of these concerns the problem of turnround in tractor cultivation, as illustrated in Figure 6.2. If two adjacent arable fields are separated by a hedge and the number of turns needed to plough both of them is 28, removal of

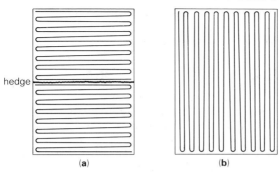

(a) (b)

Figure 6.2 The effect of removing a hedge on the number of tractor turns in cultivating a field:[52] (a) before, 28 turns; (b) after, 20 turns.

the hedge will reduce the figure to 20 – a saving of 29 per cent in fuel consumption and the tractorman's time. But the real situation can be more complex. Larger fields permit the use of wider cultivators drawn by more powerful tractors moving at greater speeds. The effect of the three variables, width of cultivator, speed and field size, on work rate can produce the comparisons shown in Figure 6.3. It will be seen that the graphs of productivity are almost flat at the lowest values but rise steeply at the higher areas. In theory at least, the greater the uninterrupted area of ground available for cultivation the better. Incidentally, less turning means a corresponding decrease in soil compaction inhibiting drainage, which can be a serious matter on heavy ground.

A further variable influencing the efficiency of cultivation is the shape of a field. Table 6.1 shows the estimated time taken by a tractorman to cultivate a 10 ha field of different measurements. It will be seen that, for a maximum saving of time in cultivation, a field needs to be a thin rectangle, since this requires the fewest

Table 6.1 Effect of field shape on the time required to cultivate 10 ha.[52] The square is used as a basis for comparison (index) and given an arbitrary value of 100.

Field shape	Minutes per hectare	Index
square	56.6	100
rectangle (2 : 1)	54.0	95
rectangle (4 : 1)	52.4	93
sides not parallel	59.5	105

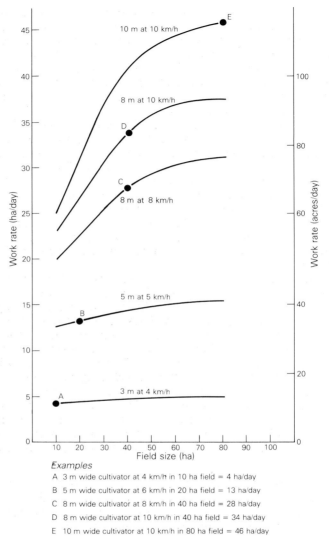

Examples

A 3 m wide cultivator at 4 km/h in 10 ha field = 4 ha/day

B 5 m wide cultivator at 6 km/h in 20 ha field = 13 ha/day

C 8 m wide cultivator at 8 km/h in 40 ha field = 28 ha/day

D 8 m wide cultivator at 10 km/h in 40 ha field = 34 ha/day

E 10 m wide cultivator at 10 km/h in 80 ha field = 46 ha/day

Figure 6.3 Combined effect on a tractorman's work rate of larger fields, wider implements and higher speeds.[52]

turns per hectare. Any irregularities such as the sides of the field not being parallel will tend to reduce efficiency, since pieces will be left over requiring separate treatment. This is the situation that obtains in most fields to varying extents. The smaller the field, the greater will be the relative effects of irregularities such as indentations and obstacles like electricity pylons. For these reasons, farmers are tempted to remove any hedges that produce awkward corners and triangles.

In economic terms, there is no doubt that large fields confer great benefits. But in achieving these benefits, we must also take into account the capital expenditure needed to grub up hedges and to purchase the new larger equipment. Clearly, costs and financial returns vary considerably from one farm to another. In general, the larger the farm, the greater the benefits are likely to be. As a result of the Cambridge research,[52] it has been established without doubt that the enlargement of fields and investment in bigger machinery is, indeed, an economic proposition and that the costs involved can be recouped in a relatively short period of time.

While accepting in principle the desirability of larger fields, the question has been raised[7] as to whether there is not an optimum size beyond which expansion could actually be disadvantageous. For instance, the topography of Britain is very different from that of the American prairies and needs to be partitioned accordingly. The view now widely held is that the upper economic limit lies somewhere within the range of 18–20 ha (45–50 acres), which is sufficient to accommodate large machinery and to ensure the various benefits outlined above. Unlike the corn belts of the USA and Canada, where large teams of machines can work side by side, the fields of Britain, no matter what their size, will seldom accommodate more than two tractormen at the same time, and often only one. In this context, excessively large fields have two kinds of disadvantage:

(a) On the practical side, much time can be wasted on such activities as returning vehicles to refuel and reload.
(b) Psychologically, there is the ergonomic disadvantage for the driver of a monotonous and unending furrow.

On the other hand, there is no doubt that some hedge removal is inevitable. Small fields of up to about 2.5 ha (6 acres) need to be enlarged say to 6–8 ha (15–20 acres) in order to make them economically viable. In some parts of England there is evidence that the emphasis on intensive cereal production and therefore the need for the largest fields may well be changing towards rotations involving crops such as rape, legumes or leys. This suggests that further field enlargement and hedge removal could be slowing down. It has been estimated[21] that during the period 1966–70 the overall destruction was of the order of 3200 km (2000 miles) a year. However, local investigations by the Countryside Commission suggest that in some areas it may still be a good deal higher. Clearly, this is an issue on which accurate local information is badly needed.

Hedges occupy potentially cultivable land

In the context of the desirability of larger fields discussed above, another reason advanced in favour of hedge removal is the need to use all land that is potentially cultivable. As a rough estimate, the removal of 400 m of hedgerow can liberate as much as 0.1 ha for cropping. Put another way, 1 ha of land is lost per 6 km of hedges (1 acre per 1½ miles). In the West Country, particularly Devon, hedges are frequently wide and grow on banks. Here their loss to agriculture is of the order of 1 ha per 2 km (1 acre per ½ mile) of hedgerow.

The economics and practicalities of land reclamation through hedge removal are not easy to evaluate precisely. However, as field size increases, the gains achieved by hedge clearance become progressively less.[14] Thus in a 40 ha (100 acre) area divided into 20 fields of 2 ha (5 acres) each, 1.1 ha (2.6 acres) would be gained by removing all the hedges, assuming they were 1.8 m (6 feet) wide. If the field size was 20 ha (50 acres), the gain in the two fields would be 0.3 ha (0.8 acres), while with a single 40 ha (100 acre) field, the increase would be only 0.2 ha (0.6 acres). With increasing field size, there is thus a drop in gain of land from 2.6 to 0.6 per cent. At the lowest level the labour and expense involved in grubbing up the hedges would hardly be worthwhile.

Such an argument suggests that the optimum figure for field size is about 20 ha (50 acres), which agrees with that arrived at on grounds of machine efficiency and ergonomic considerations and discussed above.

Finally, before embarking on a programme of uprooting hedgerows, a farmer needs to consider whether the economic gain is more important than the benefits that the hedges would have provided. This is a difficult question to which we will return in the next section (p. 132).

Hedges are reservoirs of weeds and crop pathogens

It is not so long ago that cornfields scarlet with poppy flowers (mostly the corn poppy, *Papaver rhoeas*) were a familiar sight in July. Today they are almost unknown. Two factors have contributed to this change, the improved screening of seed and the effectiveness of modern herbicide sprays, which are particularly effective against broad-leaved annuals. Arable land is constantly being disturbed through ploughing and harrowing, so the process of plant succession never proceeds very far. It is not surprising, therefore, to find that most of the familiar cornfield colonists are annuals. These include the corn buttercup (*Ranunculus arvensis*), corn cockle (*Agrostemma githago*), corn gromwell (*Buglossoides arvensis*) and corn marigold (*Chrysanthemum segetum*). All are now on the decline and rarely found on land subjected to intensive cultivation.

By contrast, hedgerows and verges, with the exception of the disturbed areas bordering thoroughfares, provide a more stable environment in which succession has usually proceeded beyond the annual stage. Herbaceous perennials such as cow parsley, hogweed and stinging nettles are unlikely to be able to colonise cornfields and are seldom found there. The assertion that hedgerows and verges harbour agricultural weeds is therefore hardly justified.

Paradoxically, there is some evidence that a certain number of weeds among a crop may actually be a benefit. Investigations of the incidence of larvae of the small white butterfly (*Pieris rapae*) and their predators on crops of brussels sprouts[53] showed that, when weeds were present, the numbers of potential predators, particularly carnivorous beetles and harvest mites, were greater than on weed-free ground. This led to an increased mortality of caterpillars. It could be argued that, where weeds in crops are shown to be beneficial, they should not be destroyed; indeed, they might even be encouraged! But in adopting such a policy, it would be important to ensure that any weeds tolerated were neither the food plants of the animal vectors of pathogens nor the harbours of the pathogens themselves, particularly fungi.

This brings us to a kindred complaint against hedgerows and verges, that they are harbours of disease vectors and pathogenic organisms. These are difficult issues to evaluate with any precision. A classic instance of such an association is that of the barberry and the fungus causing black rust in cereals, but with the present rarity of the plant host and increase in the effectiveness of fungicide sprays this is now of historical interest only.

127

A genuine problem that is still with us is the disease fireblight caused by the bacterium *Erwinia amylovora*. This is an infection largely confined to pears and evidently occurs through the flowers. It causes browning of the leaves and stems in midsummer and a reduction in yield. The disease attacks several garden shrubs such as *Cotoneaster*, and also hawthorns in hedges, which therefore provide a harbour of infection. How the bacterial spores travel from infected plants to the flowers of the pear is uncertain, but they are probably partly wind-borne and partly carried by pollinating insects such as bees and hoverflies. It could be argued that we should follow the example of the elimination of barberry in the USA and grub up all hawthorns in the vicinity of orchards. Bearing in mind the range of other plants that harbour the disease, it is at least questionable whether this would be an effective remedy. And once lost, the hawthorn hedges could not be replaced in the short term, so any benefits they confer would be lost.

Many diseases of agricultural crops are known to be transmitted by insects, a typical example being the yellowing of sugar-beet due to infection by a virus carried by the aphid, *Mysus persicae*. This can result in a reduction of crop yield of between 5 and 10 per cent. Two factors have been shown to play a part in determining the severity of an attack. Variations in wind speed evidently influence considerably the rate of spread of the disease due to the effect on the powers of dispersion of the winged aphids. Comparisons of open country and areas enclosed by hedgerows and other windbreaks have revealed striking differences in the densities and rates of dispersion of aphid carriers (**vectors**). A second factor of importance has been the density of insect predators, particularly the carnivorous larvae of ladybird beetles such as *Coccinella septempunctata* and *Adalia bipunctata*. Where these have been high, the incidence of yellowing disease has been comparatively slight.

Of recent years, another classic example of insect-borne infection has been Dutch elm disease (Fig. 6.4) caused by the fungus *Ceratostomella ulmi*, the vector being the elm bark beetle (*Scolytus scolytus*). Trees infected by the fungus seldom survive, and the disease, introduced originally in logs from Holland, is estimated to have destroyed at least 40 per cent of our total elm population of about 23 million trees. It may well be asked why biological control by predators appears to have been so ineffective on this occasion. The answer is unknown, but it could be that one reason for the spread of the disease was the comparative

Figure 6.4   Typical casualties of Dutch elm disease.

(a)

(b)

Figure 6.5   Lackey moth (*Malacosoma neustria*): (a) larvae in their characteristic web – they feed on a variety of hedgerow plants, particularly hawthorn; (b) the adult moth.

immunity of wood-boring insects such as *Scolytus* to attacks by predators from outside.

There is no doubt that hedges and verges harbour vast numbers of potential insect pests such as aphids and defoliating caterpillars of moths like the lackey (*Malacosoma neustria*) (Fig. 6.5). These are usually held in check by an equally large range of insectivores, both invertebrate and vertebrate. How these two entities will interact in a particular situation it is impossible to say, since many unknown variables are involved. But one thing is certain; in attempting to predict the likely influence of hedgerows and verges on the promotion and transmission of pests, we must think in terms not just of the significance of individual species but of that of the whole ecosystem.

Hedges are reservoirs of herbivorous mammals

Just as hedges can, on occasions, be reservoirs of crop pathogens, so they can house considerable populations of herbivorous mammals. Among these, the rabbit used to be by far the most destructive, but with the advent of myxomatosis its populations have been much reduced. As we saw earlier (p. 78), the various species of voles are subject to great fluctuations in numbers, and at their highest density can cause immense damage to agricultural crops. Reference to Figure 6.1 shows that hedges also house a range of carnivores that rely on small rodents for their prey and assist in controlling their density. These include mammals such as the fox, stoat and weasel and birds such as owls. As above, it is important to gauge the effectiveness of these predators in terms of the ecosystems to which they belong. As a source of refuge, stoats and weasels require the dense undergrowth characteristic of many hedge banks. The use of universal herbicides such as paraquat to kill all the vegetation round the edges of fields and at the base of hedges is harmful in eliminating the habitats of beneficial mammals. Again, owls require trees in which to perch and nest, and these are an important component of all agricultural land. Their removal for timber can have unfortunate consequences in relaxing the predation pressure on potential vertebrate pests. In general, hedgerow trees provide a poor crop and their erratic distribution and difficulty of access can make the task of felling hardly worthwhile. Apart from their ecological importance in housing valuable predators, they have considerable aesthetic value and there is a strong case not only for their retention but for additional plantings in field corners and areas of marginal land. This is now established policy in many parts of the country.

The shading effect of hedges reduces production

It is sometimes claimed that the shade cast by hedgerows has a significant effect on crop production, and this is therefore an argument in favour of their removal. There is no doubt that the vegetation on the north- and south-facing sides of a hedgerow can vary appreciably, as is illustrated in Figure 2.11. The degree of light reduction depends upon the height of the hedge (h). Its effect on crops is found to be appreciable only up to a distance of $(1–2) \times h$ from the base of the bank.[14] Whereas the influence on crops such as cereals can be considerable, that on grass is much less. Clearly the siting of hedges can be significant; those running east–west cast more shade overall than those running north–south. The ideal situation is therefore where the north-facing side of a hedge borders non-agricultural land such as a wide ditch, road or track.

In judging the economic significance of shading by hedges, we must also take into account its potential advantages. Where livestock are concerned, particularly in open areas, a source of shade can be an important requirement in hot weather. Again, while hedges can cast shade, they can also act as windbreaks, providing shelter belts with their associated advantages. These will be discussed further in the next section.

Hedges are a financial liability

Even with modern mechanical methods such as flails (p. 148), the maintenance of hedges is a costly business and regarded by some as a financial liability and an unproductive use of labour. An alternative is to dispense with hedges and opt for fences instead. The arguments for and against such a policy need not concern us here, but they are nonetheless important issues. Suffice it to add that all forms of agricultural barrier require capital outlay to establish them, and also recurrent expenditure on maintenance and replacement. To quote actual costs would mean little as these are constantly changing. But when they are assessed and the relative merits of hedges and fences evaluated in financial terms, there appears to be little to choose between them. Clearly, a change from one to the other has considerable ecological implications, but whether the ecological losses outweigh the marginal economic benefits is a matter for careful consideration.

Supposed advantages of hedgerows

Hedgerows act as valuable windbreaks

The fact that windbreaks of all kinds, both hedges and trees, can provide useful shelter for livestock in winter from wind, rain and snow, and from the sun in summer, is self-evident and needs little qualification. But with arable land the situation is more complex. As we saw earlier (p. 131), the shade cast by hedges is of marginal importance in agriculture and appreciable effects of light loss on arable crops do not extend beyond a distance of $(1-2) \times h$ from the hedge base. They are, therefore, only likely to be significant when a hedge is high, say over 3 m (10 ft), or if it contains numerous large trees.

An objective assessment of the effects of wind and its associated variables, temperature, humidity and evaporation, is more difficult. One of the principal problems in evaluating the effects of wind is that it seldom blows in the same direction and at the same speed for long. In studies of the wind pattern in the vicinity of an ash coppice near Walford (Herefordshire) over a five-month period, variations in mean monthly wind direction (relative to the north) were recorded ranging from 226° to 017°, a band of 151°. Over the same period, the wind speed fluctuated between 174 and 256 knots, a variation of 82 knots and a mean monthly figure of 221 knots.[54]

In the vicinity of a windbreak, such as a hedge, the local microclimate can be influenced considerably by the nature of the barrier itself. Impermeable barriers such as walls provide protection over a smaller area than permeable ones such as hedgerows, as is illustrated in Figure 6.6. When wind strikes a solid object, such as a wall, it is carried over the top and drops down quickly to ground level on the other side with its speed only slightly reduced. In addition, a low-pressure area often builds up on the leeward (downwind) side, and this can produce turbulent eddy currents with speeds even higher than the original gust. With a permeable barrier, such as a hedge, a proportion of the air is also deflected upwards and over the top. But some also filters through the hedge and this slow-moving column prevents the build-up of turbulence due to eddy currents and can extend leewards for a considerable distance before it attains its former speed once more. Curiously, there is also a build-up of slower-moving air like a cushion on the windward (upwind) side of the barrier. For a moderately permeable hedge, the protection afforded may extend to $5 \times h$ to the windward side and $20 \times h$ to the leeward

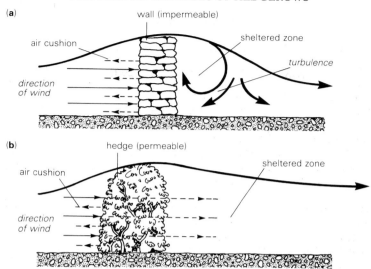

Figure 6.6 Shelter from the wind provided by (a) an impermeable barrier such as a wall and (b) a permeable barrier such as a hedgerow. Filtering of the air through a hedge provides a greater range of shelter than a wall.

side. As a rough rule of thumb, the permeability of a hedge should be of the order of 40 per cent, giving a reduction in wind speed of around 20 per cent and appreciable shelter leewards of 8–12 times the height of the hedge (8–12) $\times$ h.

The permeability of living windbreaks varies greatly not only on account of their composition but as a result of the different kinds of maintenance and the season (with or without leaves). In the ash coppice mentioned earlier,[54] shelter was lost somewhere between $3 \times h$ and $6 \times h$ due to the relatively narrow belt of trees and the distances between them. Some woods are so dense that they can behave as impermeable barriers and give only limited shelter.

The length of a hedge is also important in determining its effectiveness as a windbreak. If it is too short, a substantial body of air will flow round the ends, destroying much of the shelter that would otherwise have been achieved. As a rough rule, in order to ensure maximum shelter, a hedge should be at least 20 times as long as it is high. Winds can vary greatly in direction even over a short period. For this reason fields need to be protected by

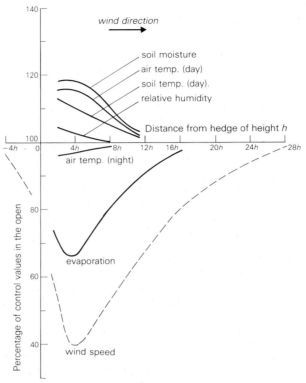

Figure 6.7 The effect of shelter on various climatic factors.[21] The main effect is a reduction in wind speed, which in turn largely governs the other variables.

hedges on all sides if maximum sheltering effects are to be obtained.

Associated with windspeed are a number of other environmental variables that can have significant effects on crop growth, such as temperature, humidity and evaporation. The significance of wind on temperature is well illustrated by the findings in an ash coppice (quoted earlier), where a variation of some 17°C occurred between microhabitats exposed to the wind and those sheltered from it. The relationship between these variables is summarised in Figure 6.7.

THE EFFECTS OF SHELTER

The effects of windbreaks on crop growth are of three kinds:

(a) reduction in the eroding force of the wind;
(b) raising the temperature of the soil; and
(c) influencing soil humidity by reducing the rate of evaporation.

As in all ecological situations, physical factors seldom exert their effects alone, but do so in varying combinations with one another. The evaluation of these effects is always difficult and needs to be approached with some caution. Variation in crop yield is a matter of great economic significance, so it is not surprising to find that numerous studies have been conducted on the influence of windbreaks in different parts of the world. Unfortunately, these have been based mainly on parts of Europe, Russia and the USA, where conditions are often very different from our own. The gains resulting from shelter have varied sensationally, ranging from 167 per cent in apple crops in Norway, 68 per cent in grassland in Hungary and 40 per cent in grain in the USSR to 6 per cent in sugarbeet in Germany.[55] A typical example of the relationship between hedge length and crop yield of wheat, rye and potatoes in Schleswig-Holstein is summarised below in Table 6.2.[49]

Are the crop increases recorded abroad likely to be a feature of Britain as well? The answer almost certainly is no. Pollard *et al.*[21] have reviewed the possibilities and conclude that, under the usual conditions prevailing on most of our farms, any increases are likely to be marginal. In many of the countries where studies have been made, although the climate and topography may be similar to our own, the types of soil are different. These are pre-

Table 6.2   Effect of hedge length on crop yield in Schleswig-Holstein.[49]

Hedge length (m/ha)	Increase in yield (%)		
	Winter wheat	Winter rye	Maincrop potatoes
20	5.0	3.6	5.0
30	6.7	5.1	7.3
40	10	7.2	10
50	15	9.5	13
60	19	12	15
70	26	14	17
80	35	17	20

dominantly light and sandy, and subject to rapid drying and low humidity. The effect of shelter belts is therefore primarily to increase soil moisture, a problem that hardly exists in this country. Special cases are the tiny bulb fields of Cornwall and the Isles of Scilly, which are bounded by semipermeable dry stone walls and hedges of such shrubs as *Pittosporum* (imported from New Zealand) and *Escallonia*. Although there are no quantitative data available, it may well be that shelter plays an appreciable part in the growth of early crops of flowers.

It is sometimes claimed that the wholesale removal of hedges could lead to soil erosion on a scale comparable with the American prairies or the Russian steppes, but this is an exaggeration. Over most of Britain the soils are relatively moist and heavy with clay and humus, with the result that wind erosion is minimal. The problem becomes more serious in the East Anglian fens, where serious 'blows' of the peaty soils are a comparatively frequent occurrence. Again, the sandy soils of Norfolk and Suffolk are subject to periodic erosion in spite of the shelter belts of pine trees that were planted in the last century.

Turning to hedgerow animals, those most likely to be affected by varying wind speeds are the weak fliers such as aphids, flies and small Hymenoptera (stinging insects). Extensive research[56] confirms what we might have expected, that the dominant influence on insect distribution in hedges is the diversity of the vegetation. Where this is rich and the attraction to insect colonists is therefore high, the effect of wind on distribution is correspondingly low. Conversely, where diversity is low and a relatively simple plant community exists, the windbreak effect is increased. Management practices affecting the physical structure and floral composition of hedgerows can therefore play an important part in influencing insect distribution.

As to the movements of the insects themselves, studies[57] have shown that, when infestations of small insects such as aphids are blown into a field from elsewhere, as often happens in spring, the greatest concentrations are at $(2-4) \times h$ to leeward and can extend up to $10 \times h$. The aerial density of potentially beneficial insects such as parasitic Hymenoptera, which breed or feed in a hedge, evidently falls off rapidly with increasing distance from it. Thus, although primary infestation of crops by insects and pests may be aided by hedges, populations nearby are more likely to be checked than those further away. In a situation where conditions can vary greatly from place to place, it is not surprising to find that firm conclusions are elusive. The best that can be said at present is that hedgerows harbour many insect populations, some pests and others beneficial. Wind can be an important factor in the dispersal of both, so the more windbreaks there are and the greater their effect the better.

Hedges are beneficial ecosystems

In the previous section we considered the effects of wind on particular groups of weakly flying organisms such as aphids possessing the potentiality for crop damage. But as we saw earlier, species do not exist alone but as part of complex interacting systems of relationships that we call ecosystems. Occupying the higher trophic levels, we find more powerful individuals such as the larger invertebrates, birds and mammals, which are unaffected by windbreaks and their effects. When a swarm of aphids is blown from a hedgerow onto an adjoining crop, they will be followed sooner or later by at least part of the ecosystem to which they previously belonged. This will include their principal predators, ladybird beetles, and also an assortment of flies (Diptera) such as robber flies (Asilidae), which feed on a wide range of small insects, and hoverflies (Syrphidae), whose larvae are carnivorous. These in turn will attract the numerous species of insectivorous birds that are habitual colonists of hedges (see Fig. 6.1). Again, we must not overlook the less overt but nonetheless far-reaching effects of many parasites, such as the minute wasps and flies that attack a wide range of other insect species, some of which are themselves parasites. Although we have little idea of the magnitude of the influence of these organisms, their action may well be fundamental in preserving an ecological balance **(biological control)**.

So the extent of the benefits conferred on agriculture by hedgerow ecosystems and the balance of friends and foes among these populations remains uncertain. No doubt it varies greatly from one locality to another. In our present state of knowledge, the maintenance of diversity would appear to be the wisest policy for farmers, providing a potent argument for the retention of hedges and the benefits they confer whenever possible.

Hedges are important ecological reservoirs

In their ecological make-up, hedges are essentially an extension of woodland. Sometimes they have remained physically attached to it; more often they are quite separate. Hedgerow communities include about half the total species of British lowland mammals and at least 14 out of the 91 recognised species of birds (many more are periodic visitors). Together they represent part of a complex ecosystem (see Fig. 6.1), which includes vast numbers of invertebrates, particularly insects. These, in turn, depend upon a wide range of plants.

There is no doubt, therefore, that hedges are important reservoirs of plant and animal life. What are the effects of their removal? The diversity of the bird populations provides a useful parameter for gauging the results of change, and this has been used on a number of occasions. For instance, a study was carried out[58] on 80 ha (200 acres) of arable land at Carlton, Cambridgeshire, during a period of increasing cereal production and a reduction in roots, leys, beans, pasture and rough ground. At the same time, there was a 30 per cent reduction in the area of hedges and woods. The changes in the bird species present are summarised in Table 6.3. Balancing the total species gained against those lost, there was evidently a slight decrease in the overall diversity of birds. Nonetheless, the variety of populations present was still high.

A quadrupling of field size from say 10 to 40 ha (25 to 100 acres) involves a reduction of hedge length by about half.[58] But if the remaining hedges are well distributed and allowed to grow, there is no need for a reduction in the number of bird species. Further, the addition of new belts of trees or small copses can bring about a substantial increase in the diversity of populations. On the other hand, the total clearance from farmland of all hedges and woods inevitably results in a faunal and floral wasteland with few species remaining apart from skylarks and lapwings. Pursuing this idea further, it has been claimed that the total removal from the British rural scene of all hedgerows would result in the extinction of a number of bird species. With the exception of certain game birds, particularly the partridge, which requires special conditions for nesting afforded by hedges, it is doubtful if any species would, in fact, succumb *provided* an ade-

Table 6.3 Changes in bird species on 80 ha (200 acres) of arable land at Carlton (Cambridgeshire), 1960–63 and 1971–72.[52]

	Summer	Winter
species gained	9	6
species increased	8	14
unchanged	23	13
species decreased	20	14
species lost	6	12

quate supply of woodland remained. Wholesale hedge destruction would by unlikely to lead to a reduction in species diversity but it would inevitably cause a considerable drop in the size of populations.

In favour of hedges, it is sometimes also claimed that they provide valuable corridors for the dispersal of animal populations and their distribution over a wide area, thereby avoiding excessive competition for available resources. While this is undoubtedly true in some situations, in the context of the previous discussion it appears to be a factor of only secondary ecological importance.

Hedges provide refuges from the effects of intensive agriculture

A special example of the issues discussed above concerns the effects of intensive agricultural practice such as the ploughing of land and planting of leys at roughly four-yearly intervals. Previously, pastureland tended to remain for years virtually immune to ploughs and chemicals, as we find in parts of France today, but in Britain this is rarely so. No sooner have grassland ecosystems begun to establish themselves than they are destroyed once more by ploughing and fertilisers. Sensitive indicators of such changes are the grassland Satyrine butterflies. Until recently the marbled white (*Melanargia galathea*) was commonly found in agricultural fields; now it is a comparative rarity there. The meadow brown (*Maniola jurtina*) (Fig. 4.7c), also a habitual colonist of meadowland, is now frequently restricted to strips of grass bordering hedgerows and verges, where it tends to overlap the habitat of the ringlet (*Aphantopus hyperanthus*) (Fig. 4.7b) and even the hedge brown (*Pyronia tithonus*) (Fig. 4.7a).

The widespread practice of monocrop cultivation has also had drastic effects on the animal populations of fields by restricting the diversity of food available to them. As a consequence, many species (particularly insects) that previously enjoyed a wider distribution have now taken refuge in hedges, where they continue to occupy vital sections of the food webs on which the indigenous birds and mammals depend. Incidentally, the same function is performed by areas of rough ground (marginal land) on farmland which, for a variety of reasons, are not amenable to cultivation. Such areas may well become increasingly important for conservation in the future.

Hedgerows have ethical and aesthetic significance

Of recent years, there has been a marked increase in public interest in the countryside, as is indicated by the rapid rise in membership of organisations associated with it. Country Nature Conservation Trusts (Fig. 6.8) are a typical example, which have increased their following from 800 to 155 000 over a period of 28 years. Comparable increases have occurred in kindred organisations such as the Royal Society for the Protection of Birds, the National Trust and the Ramblers' Association. The stimulus to join these groups has emanated from several different directions, such as the media, particularly programmes on television, and a greater mobility resulting from increased affluence coupled with more opportunities for leisure.

There is no doubt that one of the main attractions of organisations concerned with the countryside and its preservation derives from a widespread feeling for the ethical and aesthetic aspects of conservation as well as for its significance in purely

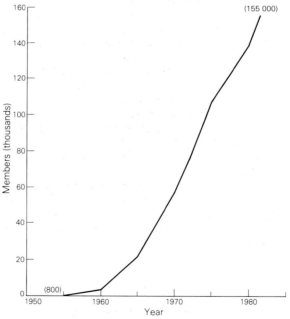

Figure 6.8 Membership of County Trusts for Nature Conservation, 1955–83.

140

utilitarian terms. Arguments based on people's morals and feelings are not easy to translate into rational terms. They centre round the realisation that man is in a position of stewardship as a custodian of nature and his environment. It is therefore morally wrong to bring about wholesale destruction of the landscape, its plants and animals. But utilitarian considerations are not easy to exclude from ethical ones. Having contributed to the preservation of the environment in all its aspects, have we not the right to use it as an amenity? True, the interests of amenity will sometimes conflict with those of preservation, and this is one of the headaches with which conservationists have to contend.

Aesthetic arguments for the conservation of aspects of the environment such as hedges are equally difficult to define in rational terms. They include a range of sensory experiences such as sights, smells, sounds and movements, indeed everything that characterises the countryside. Here again, utilitarian considerations are strong, for it is the pleasure that people derive from the country and its wildlife that causes them to wish to retain them. Moreover, what is beautiful to some is not necessarily so to others. Such ideas have been expressed for many hundreds of years in prose and verse by historians and poets. Even over historic time the environment of Britain has greatly changed at the hands of man from predominant woodland, to open fields, then small enclosures followed by an opening up of the land once more. The process is still continuing today. Clearly, we must not oppose change where it is to the material benefit of society, particularly if it causes minimal upset to the existing environment. But would we, or should we, be prepared to accept a landscape without colour, birdsong and the sounds of trees, dominated by arterial roads and concrete constructions. Where and how do we draw the line between extremes? The question is not new; it was posed with some vehemence at the time of the early enclosures and the arguments used then included aesthetic and ethical considerations. The *status quo* of the environment is not sacrosanct. It has changed over time and will certainly change again. What we have to decide is the direction, speed and extent of the evolutionary process.

The farmer and the environment

When discussing hedgerows and the justification for their continued existence, we are apt to forget that they were invented by farmers and landowners for two specific purposes – the marking of boundaries between one piece of property and another and the prevention of livestock from straying. Today the farmer finds himself in a somewhat paradoxical situation. What has been his private domain for centuries has suddenly become a national asset, with all that that implies. As we have seen in this chapter, for the farmer hedgerows and the verges associated with them have both advantages and disadvantages, the balance between them being far from clear-cut and depending to a large extent on local circumstances. Viewed by the public, hedgerows form an essential ingredient of the British countryside and, no matter what their economic value, they must be preserved. These sometimes conflicting viewpoints represent the situation as we find it today. How it can be resolved, indeed if it is resolvable, is the issue we will consider in the next two chapters.

7

Problems of conservation

Discussion of issues associated with conservation is sometimes clouded by a misunderstanding of the precise meaning of the word and its confusion with preservation, which is not the same thing. The distinction between them and the essential features of each can best be illustrated by two simple examples. Suppose we wish to retain a piece of downland in its existing state with an abundance of low-growing plants such as trefoils, vetches and orchids. We might decide to erect a fine-mesh wire netting fence around the area, thereby excluding all trespassers, including vertebrate herbivores such as rabbits and voles. In a few years' time we would be faced with a rank growth of vegetation consisting largely of coarse grasses and thistles, the low-growing species we wished to preserve having been almost completely exterminated in the struggle for survival. Passive preservation would have succeeded in excluding the very organisms responsible for maintaining the downland in its previous state.

Conservation involves a more dynamic approach in that it aims, as far as possible, to take all relevant ecological factors into account. But it is more than just an ecological exercise, as the second example illustrates. An acre of farmland was bordered by a large growth of scrub consisting mainly of hawthorn and other small bushes such as rose and bramble. Total removal would have been too expensive, so it was decided to cut lanes 5 m wide through the scrub, letting in the light and encouraging the growth of herbaceous plants on either side. This, in turn, would increase the size and diversity of the butterfly populations. Trial cuttings showed that, even after a year, substantial changes could be achieved. But in order to keep the growth of the vegetation in check, it was necessary to cut each lane at least three times a year – twice during the summer and once in autumn. Ideally, some 20 intersecting lanes were needed, each about 50 m long. But with the limited mowing resources available, this would have necessitated reducing the number of cuts to only one a year. It was therefore decided to reduce the number of lanes to eight, thereby ensuring that each could be cut three times.

The above is typical of the kind of problem faced by those involved in the conservation of wildlife. It consists essentially of three elements:

(a) An appreciation of the situation in ecological terms.
(b) The design of a management plan to achieve the desired ecological aims. This frequently involves making decisions.
(c) The practical implementation of the management plan.

Of these, (c) invariably poses the greatest problems, since the degree of success achieved depends nearly always upon the availability of resources, particularly labour and money. It is a sad fact that, wherever nature reserves in Britain have deteriorated, as many have, the cause has almost invariably been defective management, usually resulting from inadequate funding.

Hedgerows and conservation

The conservation of hedgerows frequently requires the resolution of conflicting viewpoints. Farmers tend to regard them as a liability, while conservationists are anxious to promote their survival as sanctuaries for wildlife and an amenity for the public. Like all living communities, hedgerows and verges are dynamic systems subject to continual change as a result of ecological forces such as competition and fluctuations in population density. But, being man-made, by far the most powerful influence on their status and survival is human.

How, then, are we to reconcile rival interests and arrive at a satisfactory compromise? There is no single answer, since every situation is different. However, there are certain guiding principles that can help us towards at least a partial solution of our problem, and it is with these that we shall be concerned in this chapter.

Being complete ecosystems, hedges include a wide range of ecological niches. The nature and extent of these, and therefore the species able to occupy them, depend on a variety of environmental factors such as the proportion of trees, hedge length, width and height, the existence and size of ditches and the density of vegetation, to mention only a few. In short, the overall attractiveness of hedges as habitats for plants and animals, as we have seen in the context of game birds such as partridges (p. 83), depends both on their quantity and their quality. This idea has been extended more widely to a number of other bird species and studied extensively.[59] Since hedgerows are, in a sense, extensions of the woodland environment, it is not surprising to find that the presence of trees in their vicinity or as parts of the hedges themselves exerts a significant influence on the number of bird species present. Thus Arnold[59] has estimated in an area of East Anglia that no less than 42 per cent of the variation in the number of species recorded in hedges in winter and 35 per cent in summer was attributable to the characteristics of the surroundings. Of these, trees exerted by far the greatest influence. In general, the greater the area of woodland, the fewer bird species are seen in neighbouring hedges. This is particularly true in winter, where trees provide the most important source of food. In their absence, insectivorous species such as tits are forced to forage in hedges as a second best alternative.

Similar findings relate to the number of territories established by birds in hedgerows during the breeding season. The greater the area of woodland in the vicinity, the less the number of territories in hedges. This generalisation did not, however, apply to non-arboreal species such as blackbirds, song thrushes and robins.

Again, the characteristics of the hedges themselves influence bird colonisation. Blackbirds and song thrushes favour tall, bushy hedges without trees, while tits prefer trees to be present. Wrens and robins are attracted by hedges with a diversity of shrub species, while song thrushes prefer a more uniform environment. The amount of cover available in ditches is also important for some species, such as blackbirds, but less significant for others.

From studies such as these, the predictable conclusion emerges that there is no such thing as an ideal hedge. Conditions that are favourable to one animal species may be less so to another and actually prohibitive to a third. As far as birds are concerned, a suggested specification for hedge maintenance[59] so as to increase the number of colonising species and breeding territories is as follows:

(a) Increase the average hedge height from 1.0 m to 1.4 m and width from 0.8 m to 1.2 m.
(b) Do not trim the sides of ditches every year.
(c) Trim from hedges only the last year's growth of wood.

The increased plant growth and diversity of species resulting from such practice could have the effect not only of improving the physical environment but also of increasing the populations of invertebrates, particularly the insect foods of many birds. Weed and pest problems would be likely to be marginal and exert their effects only at the edges of neighbouring crops. Indeed, it is possible that increased diversity of plant species in hedges and marginal land could actually be an advantage in diverting harmful pests and promoting others more beneficial to the farmer in particular circumstances.[60]

Hedgerow management

If allowed to grow unchecked, hedges gradually develop into small woods occupying an ever increasing area of ground (Fig. 7.1). As they grow, they become progressively thinner at the base owing to the shading effect of the vegetation above, thus ceasing to achieve one of their main functions, the control of movement by livestock. In order to preserve them as tough and impenetrable barriers, a scheme of regular care is therefore needed.[14,61]

Hedge trimming

The most usual method of hedge maintenance is periodic trimming, which, besides producing a neat and orderly appearance,

Figure 7.1 A hedge left untrimmed for 15 years.

Figure 7.2 Flail hedge cutter: (a) flail mechanism housed inside its metal cowl; (b) mounted on a tractor.

stimulates growth of side shoots and thus increases the bushiness of the hedge and its stockproof qualities. At one time, when labour was cheap and plentiful, hedge trimming was carried out entirely by hand. Today, the process is everywhere mechanical by means of flail cutters. These consist of revolving chain-like structures housed inside a metal cowl (Fig. 7.2a) and mounted on a tractor (Fig. 7.2b). The rotation of the flails chips, chews and mulches unwanted growth on hedges, verges and the banks of ditches, leaving the remains in such a finely divided state that there is little need to collect them afterwards. Indeed, by remaining on the ground they can provide a useful mulch, conserving moisture and promoting further plant growth.

The profile of a hedge is of some importance both from the point of view of its effectiveness as a barrier and windbreak, and also for saving labour in maintenance. Five of the commonest shapes are illustrated in Figure 7.3. The rectangular pattern is the most problematical. Its protagonists claim that it grows best because a large surface area on top is exposed to the sunlight. The counterargument is that the dense top casts shade on the branches below, inhibiting much of their growth and eventually killing them. The bottom of the hedge then becomes too open and no longer stockproof. The flat top also tends to accumulate snow and hedge trimmings, both of which can damage the vege-

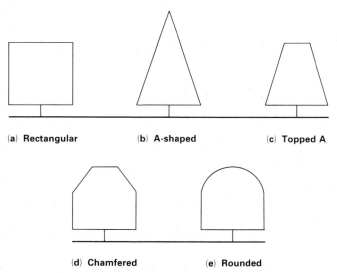

(a) Rectangular   (b) A-shaped   (c) Topped A

(d) Chamfered   (e) Rounded

Figure 7.3 Some variations in hedge profile.

148

tation underneath. The A-shaped profile has several advantages, particularly if cut to a height of about 1.8 m. Cutting is easy and requires only two runs, one each side. Its slope allows accumulations of snow and trimmings to fall off so that the hedge itself is not easily damaged. The narrow top facilitates the passage of air, causing the minimum of turbulence (see p. 132) and providing an effective windbreak. Extensive cutting at the top encourages active growth lower down, providing a firm barrier for stock and also good cover for wildlife. The high apex also facilitates the inclusion of young saplings, which are otherwise left projecting above the line of the hedge. The topped-A and chamfered types aim to combine the advantages of the other two and are both widely used, particularly in conditions where the farmer requires a bulky hedge. Their disadvantage is that they are less economical to maintain, requiring four runs of the cutter instead of two. Rounded hedges used to be a feature of farmland when all maintenance was by hand. Now they are confined almost exclusively to recreational areas such as parks and gardens.

In spite of the universal use of mechanical trimmers, different parts of the country still retain their preferences for particular hedge shapes. Thus in Yorkshire hedges tend to be tall and thin (A-shaped), while in the South the more usual patterns are topped-A or chamfered.

In the interests of public safety and of achieving satisfactory results, the Ministry of Agriculture, Fisheries and Food through the Agricultural Development and Advisory Service (ADAS) has laid down a suggested sequence of steps for mechanical trimming.[61] Since these are by no means always familiar to flail operators, it is worth enumerating them in detail:

(1) First inspect the hedge to be trimmed, assessing its condition and any saplings to be left to grow into mature trees; also look out for any wildlife features requiring special care. Look for any obstacles, such as metal objects or large trees, that could damage the machinery and send up fragments injuring bystanders or stock.

(2) Cut the verges first, being careful not to undercut the stems at the base of the hedge.

(3) Next cut the lower part of the hedge, followed by the upper part or top.

(4) Finally, rake up and burn the larger trimmings to leave a tidy site.

In general, these simple instructions seem to be followed reasonably well, but many travellers will no doubt harbour

Figure 7.4 'Save this Sapling': a young elm tagged and allowed to continue growing.

memories of roads where flail cutters have recently been at work strewn thick with debris resembling a plant battlefield.

An important aspect of hedge trimming that is understressed in the ADAS guidelines quoted above is the preservation of desirable saplings. As we saw earlier, for many animal species, particularly birds, trees form the most important component of the hedgerow flora. In their enthusiasm to produce a neat job, flail operators are tempted all too often to trim everything irrespective to the same height. Regeneration of trees cannot therefore take place, and as the older individuals die or are cut down, there is nothing to replace them. Many farmers now subscribe to the 'Save this Sapling' scheme, whereby small trees are tagged with white labels before trimming occurs and allowed to continue growing, as illustrated in Figure 7.4.

Hedge laying

Provided a hedge is trimmed regularly every two or three years, the growth of side shoots will be stimulated, vigour will be prolonged and an effective shelter will be provided for both farm animals and wildlife. However, over a period of time, hedge management follows a regular cycle, which passes through three phases:

150

(a) A young hedge is trimmed until a satisfactory shape is attained. After continual trimming, increased shade causes the base to become thin as the branches die off.

(b) The hedge is now allowed to grow to at least twice its previous height or more.

(c) It is then coppiced (cut down) or laid.

The duration of a complete cycle of trimming, growth and coppicing or laying varies from one set of conditions to another but, on average, it is about 20 years.

Coppicing is a somewhat radical method of management in that it involves cutting down the shrubs to within a few inches of the ground. Some species such as hawthorn and field maple respond well to this treatment by throwing up numerous young shoots from the base of the plants. Others like holly and blackthorn are often killed by it. The advantages of coppicing are that it is quick and therefore cheap, and also no great expertise is required. Clearly, it is inappropriate if a hedge needs to be permanently stockproof. Another disadvantage is that new growths from the cut stems tend to grow upright and therefore leave gaps between one plant and the next. These will either have to be filled in later by further planting or wire, or closed when the hedge is next laid.

The purpose of laying is partly to restore a stockproof barrier and also to rejuvenate the hedge shrubs themselves by encouraging the formation of new shoots from the base of the old stems. The procedure is highly skilled, time-consuming and therefore expensive. For this reason, and also because of the lack of trained labour, it is employed less and less.[14,61] The basic process consists of cutting but not completely severing the main stems of the young trees, and pushing them sideways so that they intermingle to form a barrier. The laying procedure has acquired a picturesque jargon as well as a fascinating diversity of cutting implements, which form a study of their own.[62] Four stages are involved:

(a) The main stems (**pleachers**), which have grown to a height of 3–3.5 m, are cut through part way with a billhook or axe and pushed over to make a barrier.

(b) Lengths of hazel or ash (**stakes**) 3.5–4.0 cm in diameter are driven into the hedge bank between the stems of the cut pleachers at intervals of 4.5–6.0 m.

(c) Lengths of pliable wood such as hazel or willow 2.5–3 m long (**binders** or **heathers**) are twisted round the top of the stakes to prevent the pleachers from springing upwards.

(a)

(b)

(c)

Figure 7.5 Laying a hedge: (a) preliminary cutting of pleachers; (b) inserting stakes; (c) binding and the finished product.

(d) The stakes are trimmed to an even finish and any projecting stems removed so as to give a tidy appearance and to avoid damage to livestock when they rub against them.

The laying technique illustrated in Figure 7.5 is of the standard or Midlands hedge, which is characteristic of much of England. However, there are numerous local variations, such as the Welsh hedge, which is designed primarily as a barrier against sheep and is therefore dense but not necessarily very high. Midlands hedges are always 'single bushed', with the pleachers laid mainly from one side with the brushy ends angled out on the other side. But many Welsh hedges are 'double bushed', with the pleachers laid from both sides and the bushy ends extending alternately one side and the other, so producing a more symmetrical and bushy appearance. Again, some Welsh hedges are thin and 'single bushed' but reinforced with quantities of deadwood cuttings, thus ensuring that all potential gaps are closed. In all, there are a dozen or so distinct Welsh styles and similar variations exist in other parts of the country as well. This is not the place for a discourse on the minutiae of laying procedures. Like the implements used, the techniques and their variants are a study on their own and have been admirably described elsewhere.[14]

Once a hedgerow has been laid, it is usually left untrimmed for the first year to allow new shoots to grow out below the cut in each pleacher. At this stage, the greatest enemies are cattle, and if the young growths are to survive the animals need to be kept away by means of a temporary fence. The hedge-laying season extends from autumn (October) to spring (May), the best time being when the sap is beginning to rise in March–April. It can therefore coincide with the height of the bird-nesting season.

Significance of marginal land

In the context of farming, marginal land includes any pieces of ground that are unsuitable for cultivation. These may be small patches of woodland, steep slopes, former quarries and obstructions of a variety of kinds. Of particular significance in the present context are the corners of fields where hedgerows intersect, frequently at rather acute angles. Such ground is often inaccessible to machines and sometimes supports a growth of rank vegetation, much of which is derived from the hedges nearby. In some areas, particularly hilly districts, marginal land can attain quite high proportions and hence contribute appreci-

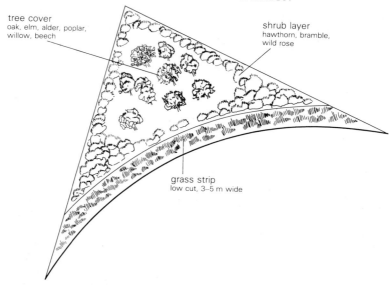

tree cover
oak, elm, alder, poplar,
willow, beech

shrub layer
hawthorn, bramble,
wild rose

grass strip
low cut, 3–5 m wide

Figure 7.6   Planting scheme for a field corner.[70]

ably to the fund of wildlife. Effective management can greatly increase this contribution, particularly at field corners. The move towards the planting of trees in such places is now well established in some parts of the country but less so in others. The Nature Conservancy Council has pursued the idea a step further and proposed a composite scheme illustrated in Figure 7.6. This consists not only of an appropriate range of trees, such as oak, elm and willow, but also a shrub layer similar in composition to the hedges nearby. Bordering the woody plants is a verge 3–5 m wide in which grasses and other herbaceous perennial species can flourish, thus enhancing the local ecosystem.

Conservation of verges

From an ecological and conservation standpoint, hedgerows and verges often form part of a continuum. Indeed, where they merge, their plant and animal populations are frequently similar. On the other hand, responsibilities for their respective maintenance are quite distinct. In general, the task of conserving most hedges falls to the farmer, while the upkeep of verges is the responsibility of local councils. The principal aims of verge management are threefold:

(a) to ensure good visibility, particularly in areas where bends are frequent and the growth of vegetation would be likely to impair the vision of motorists;

(b) to enable verges to fulfil their various material and social functions (see p. 20); and

(c) to present an appearance of general tidiness.

Maintenance is achieved by two methods, namely cutting and the application of herbicides, although the proportions in which each is used vary somewhat from one county to another.

Methods of verge maintenance

In rural areas particularly, verge maintenance is now carried out largely by cutting using mechanical flails (see p. 148), which are highly effective for the purpose. This is often combined with a tidying up of the vegetation in ditches and at the base of hedges (Fig. 7.7). Although the long-term damage to the vegetation may be small, the timing of a cutting operation can be crucial. This usually takes place in midsummer (July) and again in autumn (October). Plants such as bluebells which flower early are therefore able to set their seed and disperse it before cutting occurs. It is significant that such species have been able to extend their range in hedgerows to a striking degree of recent years in some parts of Britain such as Wiltshire. Others manage to flower and seed between cutting times, while for some an increase in range is

Figure 7.7 A hedge bank after tidying by flail cutter.

Table 7.1 Some common herbicides.

Paraquat	A total herbicide killing all green material with which it comes in contact. It is quickly broken down in the soil to harmless substances and is mostly used around houses for clearing weeds from paths and drives.
Dalapon	Only effective against narrow-leaved species such as grasses and used mainly for special purposes such as control of the reedmace (*Typha latifolia*) growing on swampy ground. It persists in the soil for 3–4 months.
Asulam	Another specialist herbicide effective against bracken and used also for the control of docks. Unfortunately, it is not selective where other ferns are concerned but is equally lethal to every species with which it comes in contact.
Garlon	The active ingredient is Triclopyr, which is particularly effective in killing nettles and docks.
Amcide	Contains ammonium sulphamate and kills brushwood and regenerating tree stumps.
Roundup	A broad-spectrum herbicide containing glyphosate. It is highly effective in controlling most herbaceous vegetation, brushwood and tree stumps.

restricted to vegetative methods only. Maintenance patterns applied regularly from year to year could, in theory, exert a powerful selective influence on the reproductive cycles of verge-dwelling plant species.

A more drastic form of maintenance involves the destruction of unwanted vegetation by chemical pesticides, and although the circumstances in which this method should be employed have been clearly stated, these are still subject to varied interpretation. The principal herbicides used are all absorbed through the leaves of plants. They can therefore be applied as sprays from vehicles and pumps of a variety of kinds. There is now a wide range of proprietary products, some of the commonest being given in Table 7.1.

Rather than killing the roadside vegetation, another method of ensuring continuing visibility throughout the plant growing season is to curtail plant growth. This approach has led to the development of growth retarders, one of the most effective being maleic hydrazide (MH). This has the effect of stopping flowering and checking vegetative growth by suppressing cell division at the growing points of the stems and leaves. The plants therefore remain short and seldom form seed, but most are not killed. MH is applied as a spray either alone or in combination with a selective herbicide, usually 2,4-D. When used alone, it is effective in retarding the growth of grasses, particularly the coarser species, producing the short sward that is often a feature of verges on the outskirts of built-up areas. Against broad-leaved plants it is relatively ineffective. While it can control the growth of umbellifers such as cow parsley (*Anthriscus sylvestris*) to some extent, it has little effect on lower-growing dicotyledons such as ribwort plantain (*Plantago lanceolata*) and creeping thistle (*Cirsium vulgare*). Another outcome of MH treatment is to reduce the level of competition between different species and hence to allow colonisation by a variety of annuals such as chickweed (*Stellaria media*).[63]

When applied by itself, 2,4-D effectively eliminates most broad-leaved plants except certain resistant species such as field scabious (*Knautia arvensis*). However, in the absence of competition from dicotyledons, the more strongly growing grasses soon take over. With MH added, control of broad-leaved species is much the same but the growth of grasses is suppressed. Some species that spread by underground stems (rhizomes) are less affected than others, and these tend to increase, such as the reflexed meadowgrass (*Puccinellia distans*).

The timing of spray application is important and the best results are obtained if this corresponds to the period of most active growth. Thus, under experimental conditions, it has been found that a mixture of MH and 2,4-D applied in early May held the vegetation in check for a considerable period and by early June it was only about 10 cm (4 in) high compared with 25 cm (10 in) for plots sprayed later.[63]

A code covering the use of pesticides of all kinds has been drawn up by the Nature Conservancy Council[64] and summarises in concise form the dangers of spraying chemicals indiscriminately. All pesticides now in general use have to be cleared by the Pesticides Safety Precautions Scheme, and this takes account not only of the effects on their intended targets but also the likely consequences of their application for wildlife. Those pesticides officially approved are listed in an annual publication produced by the Ministry of Agriculture, Fisheries and Food.

Where vegetation control is needed along roadside banks and verges, cutting is usually used rather than spraying. Circumstances where chemical control may be judged preferable include:

(a) the destruction of noxious weeds, defined under the Weeds Act of 1959, such as spear, creeping and field thistles, curled and broad-leaved docks and ragwort;

157

(b) the presence of physical obstructions, such as pylons, that would impede the movement of cutters; and

(c) difficult areas for the manoeuvring of mechanical equipment, such as steep slopes and gulleys.

The effectiveness of spraying with selective herbicides is greatly influenced by the weather. For instance, if it rains within three hours of the application of a chemical, much of it will be washed off the leaves before it has been absorbed. Again, timing is vital. Treatment usually takes place from mid-March until early May, but if it is carried out before all the weeds have started to grow, some will be unaffected. Indeed, the eventual situation may be worse than before, for in the absence of competition from the species that have been killed, the survivors often grow more vigorously than ever, necessitating a supplementary programme of cutting later in the season. The argument sometimes advanced in favour of spraying, that it is more labour saving than cutting, is seldom justified.

The extent to which the spraying of verges with selective weed-killers actually occurs varies greatly from one Local Authority to another. Of the County Councils in England and Wales circularised in 1972, 19 out of 44 stated that they never used chemical sprays or only in exceptional circumstances.[17] The remainder employed them habitually but in varying degree. It seems unlikely that the situation has changed appreciably since then.

Verge management and conservation

Relating the different methods of managing verges to the needs of conservation is not easy and requires consideration of a number of ecological factors. The cutting of perennial plants by flail seldom kills them but only impedes their life cycle. As we have seen, this applies particularly to the setting and dispersal of seed. It also has secondary effects both on the animals that depend upon those plants for their food and on their predators and parasites. Again, flailing can cause physical disturbance to birds nesting in nearby hedgerows at a critical stage in their breeding cycle.

A further problem of equating the use of herbicide sprays on roadside verges with the interests of conservation is the definition of what should be regarded as a noxious weed. Thus, among the provisions of the 1959 Weeds Act, various species of thistle are specifically stated as undesirable, yet they support a range of

158

insects, some of which are beneficial to the farmer. Again, stinging nettles are frequently targets of herbicide destruction regardless of the fact that they provide the food of such desirable species as the small tortoiseshell and peacock butterflies.

Another problem concerns the limitation of selective herbicides such as 2,4-D and MCPA, in that their selectivity amounts to no more than a discrimination between broad-leaved plants and narrow-leaved (e.g. grasses). Apart from its impact on the ecosystem as a whole, spraying results in the extermination of all the familiar flowering species, leading to conditions of dull uniformity such as characterise the verges of many of our suburban areas today.

8

What future?

As a result of public outcry and action by various pressure groups and government organisations, there is evidence that the disappearance of hedgerows may be slowing down. But in the absence of funding by public bodies such as the Nature Conservancy Council and the Countryside Commission towards hedge preservation and maintenance, which would seem to be an impossible financial burden, the removal of hedges is bound to continue (Fig. 8.1), if only at a reduced rate. The forces determining the rate of change and its extent are, as always, primarily economic.

As we saw earlier, hedges were invented by farmers in times of abundant cheap labour as the most efficient means available of marking the boundaries of property and preventing livestock from straying. Over the years, radical changes have taken place in farming strategy. The localised strip cultivations of medieval times gave way to the enclosures of the 17th and 18th centuries associated with wool production, followed by the gradual change in arable farming from a labour-intensive system to an industrial one, employing large, sophisticated machinery. Moreover, the balance of production is constantly changing in accordance with such influences as national requirements and the dictates of the European Economic Community. For instance, the ratio of milk production to that of cereals and other crops such as rape seed is something a farmer needs to keep constantly under review.

Such changes have been reflected in the state of the countryside, and this is as true today as ever. The problem facing us now is to decide how, in the interest of all concerned, we can make the best of what we have left. The future welfare of hedgerows and verges rests mainly in the hands of four groups of people – farmers, Local Authorities, conservation organisations and the

Figure 8.1 Aerial view of a modern field system (Suffolk). The dark lines in the large field show clearly where hedges have recently been removed.

general public. In the remainder of this chapter we will consider the respective responsibilities of these groups and try to assess their likely influence in the foreseeable future.

Roles of farmers

In order to meet the requirements of modern farm machinery and to use it at maximum efficiency, fields need to be large and rectangular with no difficult corners, such as acute angles, that prohibit manoeuvre. Available evidence suggests (see p. 125) that, for the conditions found in most of Britain, the optimum field size is between 15 and 20 ha (45–50 acres). Most of the changes that have taken place involving hedgerow removal have been for the purpose of field enlargement. A typical example[52] is an arable farm in Norfolk, which formerly comprised 59 small fields of assorted shapes and average size 10 ha (25 acres) (Fig. 8.2a). Removal of dividing hedges reduced the number of fields to 25 and increased their average area to over 20 ha (50 acres) (Fig. 8.2b).

It will be seen that, in spite of hedge removal, a number of awkward corners remained. Many of these, and also a few areas in the vicinity of unsightly buildings, were planted with trees, thus improving the appearance of what had formerly been a rather bare and uninteresting landscape. In the long term, it is likely that new spinneys will also have made good some of the loss of wildlife (particularly birds and insects) caused by the removal of hedges.

One of the more encouraging developments in recent years has been the establishing of the Demonstration Farms Project under the auspices of the Countryside Commission.[71] This comprises some 10 farms distributed throughout England and Wales and varying in size from 1370 to 100 ha (3425 to 250 acres). The purpose of the scheme is to help in answering the questions:

(a) Is it possible to combine profitable farming and conservation interests?

(b) What are the most cost-effective ways of managing both existing and new landscape features?

A typical example is Manor Farm, Kingston Deverill, Wiltshire,[71] comprising some 1183 ha (2958 acres) of which approximately 1130 ha (2825 acres) are cropped and stocked. This consists partly of lowland arable fields and partly of chalk downland. The remainder is made up of woods, scrub, buildings

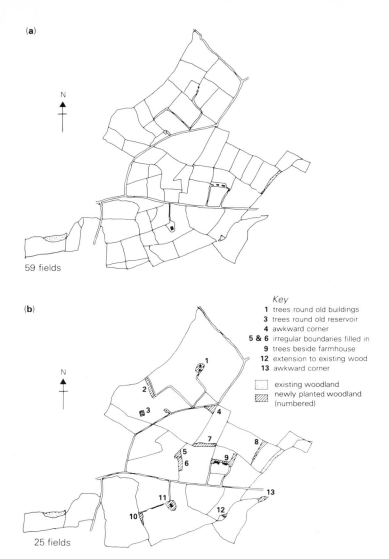

(a)

N

59 fields

(b)

N

25 fields

Key

1 trees round old buildings
3 trees round old reservoir
4 awkward corner
5 & 6 irregular boundaries filled in
9 trees beside farmhouse
12 extension to existing wood
13 awkward corner

existing woodland
newly planted woodland
(numbered)

Figure 8.2 Changes in the layout of arable fields involving an average increase in field size from 10 to over 20 ha (25 to more than 50 acres):[52] (a) before change, 59 fields; (b) after change, 25 fields.

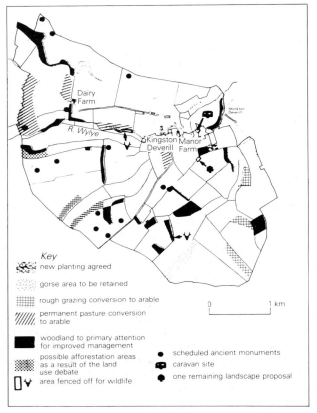

Figure 8.3 Management plan of a Demonstration Farm (Manor Farm, Kingston Deverill, Wiltshire).[71]

and roads. With the help of numerous expert organisations representing farming, landscape and wildlife interests, a management plan was drawn up. This is illustrated in Figure 8.3, and involved the following:

(a) Conserving the most valuable wildlife areas, including part of the chalk downland.
(b) Increasing the arable area by ploughing 45 ha (113 acres) of permanent pasture.
(c) Improving the management of existing woodland.
(d) Tree planting to conserve landscape and amenity by shielding new buildings and improving game coverts.

164

(e) Some hedgerow removal and amalgamation of land to increase the average field area.
(f) Careful management of hedgerows to improve their stockproofing, landscape and wildlife value. The variety of cutting regimes included laying, coppicing and flailing to A shape (see p. 148).
(g) Conservation of important archaeological features such as Bronze Age barrows found on the site.
(h) Establishment of recreational facilities such as footpaths and waymarking.

Such a scheme provides an admirable model for a comprehensive approach to farm management and evolution, and illustrates well how the sometimes conflicting interests of the farmer and the conservationist can be reconciled to the benefit of both.

The concept of the 'open farm' offering various amenities and degrees of public access is becoming more common, particularly in the South of England. In many instances, it has proved successful in improving the relationship and understanding between the farmer and the public, and it is to be hoped that such initiatives will continue.

So far we have been concerned with schemes that have involved the modification of management techniques. But there is much that a farmer can do to aid hedgerow conservation that already forms part of his existing routine. Emphasis was laid earlier (p. 153) on the importance of planting trees on marginal land, both as an eventual crop and in relation to their significance for bird and insect populations. But all too often the fact is overlooked that a fund of actively growing trees already exists in hedgerows as saplings. That these never mature is largely due to an overriding quest for tidiness and indiscriminate cutting by flail operators. Reference has already been made (p. 150) to the 'Save this Sapling' scheme now established countrywide. Wider observance of this would contribute not only to an increase in the number of trees without the cost of planting but also to the survival of the hedges associated with them.

Methods of field maintenance can also exert profound effects on surrounding hedgerows and verges. It stands to reason that, when hedging and ditching are required, these operations should not be carried out in the spring during the bird-nesting season. Most potentially dangerous of all is the practice of burning in late summer the straw stubble left behind after harvesting. An unexpected change of wind direction can all too easily lead to loss of control and irreparable damage to surrounding trees and other vegetation. Once destroyed, the replacement for a hedge is almost invariably a wire fence.

Again, in arable fields where crops are being grown, it is now widespread practice to spray a strip about a metre wide round the edge with herbicide as a means of controlling the inroads of weeds. Great care is needed on windy days not to allow these sprays to drift onto nearby hedges. Although the shrubs themselves are unlikely to be killed, the vegetation at their base can suffer serious damage, to the detriment of small mammals, certain nesting birds and most insects.

Roles of Local Authorities

Where hedges are concerned, responsibility for their management usually rests with the landowner. Only rarely is the Local Authority involved, for instance when a hedgerow has been planted on ground owned by the Local Authority. Here, the same provisions apply as for the maintenance of farm hedges discussed in the previous section.

Similar considerations apply in lesser degree to roadside ditches, since their clearance can have important implications for the prevention of flooding. Here again, the rules are the same as before (p. 155), namely that such operations should be confined to the autumn and winter so as to create the least disturbance to local ecosystems. It should be added that the need for regular cleaning may soon become a thing of the past as roads are increasingly supplied with piped drainage.

Management of verges

As we saw earlier, the maintenance of verges is largely the responsibility of local councils. Its purposes are principally to ensure adequate visibility for motorists and a tidy roadside appearance. These aims are achieved mainly by cutting with flails and to a lesser extent by the use of selective herbicides (p. 156). For the survival of wildlife, two factors are of particular importance: the times of treatment (discussed in the previous chapter), and its extent. Clearly, this will vary with the situation, particularly the overall width of the verge. At a maximum, cutting can extend not only to the whole of the verge but also to the base of the adjoining hedge and even to the hedge itself. As an optimum, a cut zone of about 60 cm (2 ft) is sufficient (Fig. 8.4), leaving much of the flora of the inner zone intact, such as the cow parsley

Figure 8.4 Verge partly cut to improve visibility. The times of cutting can be vital for wildlife.

in the photograph. In practice, the policy of different local Authorities varies; some, usually in rural areas, incline towards a restricted regime of management while others, particularly in suburban districts, favour more radical treatment.

The Countryside Commission in conjunction with the Nature Conservancy Council has suggested a code of practice[65] for the treatment of roadside verges aiming both to satisfy the requirements of practicality and to enhance the conditions for wildlife, while providing features of landscape interest. Five levels of management are envisaged.

(1) Where verges are unusually wide, for instance beside large trunk roads, portions of natural scrub and woodland should be allowed to develop and remain uncut.
(2) Rear areas of narrower verges not concerned in influencing traffic visibility should remain scrub-free and be subjected to one mowing a year, preferably in late autumn or winter.
(3) Verges adjacent to carriageways should be maintained at a maximum regulation height of 30 cm. Up to two cuttings may be needed during the growing season between early May and the end of June and possibly one also in late autumn or winter.
(4) For verges in built-up areas, it may be necessary to maintain

the vegetation at less than 30 cm height. This will require frequent cutting from early May until the end of August. It does
not, however, necessitate the elimination of all broad-leaved
plants.

(5) Where verges have special biological interest in supporting
unusual ecosystems or individual rarities, special management procedures may be necessary and agreed with the Local
Authority concerned.

A comprehensive report[17] in 1972 on road verges and their
management throughout England and Wales underlies the
diversity of approaches by councils and the differing degrees to
which they conform to the code of practice of the Countryside
Commission outlined above. Thus it was quite common along
main trunk roads for the whole extent of the verge to be cut
during the period June–August, the time of maximum growth and
flowering of most species of wild plants. Since then the situation
has certainly improved following public complaints and repre-
sentations by bodies such as County Trusts for Nature Conservation. However, in some counties there is still much room for
further improvement.

Contributions of conservation organisations

It has been argued[66] that, in the context of Britain as a whole, the
setting up of a few reserves for the preservation of wild environments together with their plant and animal populations is largely
irrelevant. Nothing short of a massive 'back to nature' movement
with a universal public awareness of and regard for wildlife could
restore a deteriorating environment. Such a view is not only
unduly pessimistic but also disregards the lessons of history.
Much of the earlier part of this book was concerned with tracing
the course of change in Britain from the Iron Age onwards, with
particular reference to the demarcation of property and control
of livestock. As our population has increased and its needs
diversified so, too, have new industries come into being and the
nature of farm management changed. Today, the claims of
wildlife have to compete with those of high-productivity farming,
industrial reorganisation, housing needs, communications and a
host of other interests. A satisfactory balance of conflicting
claims will be achieved not by attempting to reverse the course of
history but by making the best use of what we have left and ensur-

168

ing that future decisions affecting the environment are based on a thorough knowledge of their implications. One of the most encouraging features of recent years has been the increasing realisation among planning authorities and the general public that conservation in all its aspects is something we need to take seriously if we are to avoid irreparable damage to our existing environment.

Mention was made earlier (p. 118) of the phenomenal losses in our hedgerows that have occurred over the last 25 years or so following the progressive industrialisation of agriculture and the quest for ever increasing gains from the land. What is true of hedges is equally true of other wildlife habitats. Thus, roughly over the same period, we have lost through agricultural intensification 97 per cent of our herb-rich meadows previously untreated by fertilisers, 80 per cent of our chalk and limestone downlands, 40 per cent of our acidic heathland, and between 30 and 50 per cent of our ancient woodland. Similarly, of 1423 native species of flowering plants and ferns, 149 have declined by at least 20 per cent while 10 have become extinct altogether. Among birds, at least 35 breeding species have shown appreciable long-term decline[67]. The whole catalogue of destruction makes depressing reading.

At the same time, the setting up of National Parks, the designation of Areas of Outstanding Natural Beauty and the establishment of Sites of Special Scientific Interest, as well as many nature reserves organised by County Trusts for Nature Conservation, provide evidence of an increasing awareness of the need to conserve as much as possible of what we have left. The problems here are not so much ecological as managerial. It is one thing to identify an area of outstanding importance for wildlife but quite another to maintain it in its existing state or even to improve it. Unless we can devise and implement plans of management that are feasible within our limited range of resources, much of what we now have will be lost – as has already happened with some of our reserves.

The same argument applies to the survival of hedgerows and verges. If farmers are unwilling to devote the necessary funds to hedge cutting and laying, and local councils are insensitive in their policies towards the maintenance of verges and their wildlife, the outlook for the future is indeed bleak. Fortunately, there are signs of increasing wisdom and a greater willingness to collaborate with those who have the interests of the environment at heart. But we still have some way to go.

At national level, one of the largest holders of land is the

169

National Trust, set up in 1895 with power to own property in per-petuity under guarantees of Parliament. National Parks such as Exmoor, Dartmoor and Snowdonia are also extensive and, although designated by the Countryside Commission, are man-aged by the National Parks Committees of Local Authorities or the National Parks Planning Board. Some of our major national amenities are of great antiquity, such as the New Forest, which was established for hunting by William the Conqueror more than a 1000 years ago and is still subject to its own rights and admin-istration to this day. As we saw earlier (p. 169), conservation at national level has diverged along two separate paths – the protec-tion of land by the Countryside Commission and the conser-vation of wildlife by the Nature Conservancy Council (formerly the Nature Conservancy). It is indeed unfortunate that these two increasingly influential bodies should have so often acted in the past alone and even sometimes in antagonism. However, there are now encouraging signs of closer cooperation, for instance, in the establishing of model farms (p. 162) where the interests of farming, land management and wildlife preservation are brought together. Advising and lobbying government departments on every aspect of conservation and management of the environ-ment are a number of increasingly powerful independent bodies such as The Council for the Protection of Rural England, The Friends of the Earth, the Royal Society for the Protection of Birds and the Royal Society for Nature Conservation, representing the 45 or so County Trusts for Nature Conservation.

Apart from tracts of land controlled by the National Trust or designated National Parks, some 4000 Sites of Special Scientific Interest (SSSI) all over the country have been identified by the Nature Conservancy Council and designated under the provi-sions of the Wildlife and Countryside Act, 1981.[67] Many of these cover considerable areas of country. Restricted public access is sometimes permitted, but the removal of plants and animals is prohibited. At a more parochial level, the County Trusts for Nature Conservation each control and maintain numerous reserves representing habitats considered to be of particular significance in their areas, such as the chalk downland of Wiltshire, the moorland of Yorkshire and the Fens of Cambridge. Many Trusts have carried out valuable local surveys monitoring change in particular communities, such as the road verge survey conducted by the Avon Wildlife Trust. Evidence of the greatly increased public awareness of, and interest in, such activities is provided by the sensational rise in membership of County Trusts for Nature Conservation in recent years, as is illustrated in Figure 6.8.

The general public

Those with any sensitivity for their environment must often view with despair the legacy of the litter louts to many of the hedgerows and verges that border our main roads (Fig. 8.5). Bottles, plastic cartons, metal cans and paper are strewn everywhere, as are orange peel, banana skins and even human excreta. Verges are frequently used as dumping grounds for garden and building refuse, old mattresses, disused cookers and even defunct motorcars. It is sometimes claimed that, as a result of improved education and the impact of the media, the public is gradually becoming more environment-conscious. If this is so,

Figure 8.5   A farmer surveys the legacy of the litter louts.

171

the behaviour of a substantial proportion of the community still provides little evidence in support of this assertion.

The kind of damage that continues to be inflicted on the countryside, and on hedgerows and verges in particular, is of three main kinds:

(a) The breaking down of gates and hedges. The habit of climbing over gates instead of going through them, and also of leaving them unfastened, not only increases their deterioration but enables livestock to escape, providing a hazard both for themselves and for passing traffic. By the same token, scrambling through hedges can create gaps, thus reducing their effectiveness as barriers. These may take years to make good through the natural growth of the hedging shrubs.

(b) The destruction of wildlife, particularly the pillaging of birds' nests and the picking of wild flowers. In established nature reserves, steps are usually taken to conserve interesting animals such as unusual butterflies and birds, and also to prevent rare plants from having their flowers picked or being dug up. It is often forgotten by pickers of the primroses, cowslips and bluebells of our hedgerows in springtime that their activities are not only forbidden by law but are preventing these plants from forming seed, thus depriving them of their capacity to propagate and so to increase their range.

(c) Pollution, particularly by non-degradable materials such as glass bottles, plastic cartons and metal cans. Reference was made earlier to the polluted roadside verges that are all too frequently a feature of our countryside in summer. The provision of refuse bins is only a partial answer, as these require regular emptying, necessitating increased labour and added costs of maintenance. The only final solution to the problem of litter is to educate the public in the understanding that their refuse is their own responsibility. If we choose to bring containers of food to a site, the onus is on us to take the remnants away. Such a policy has been adopted in several National Parks and other beauty spots, and has met with some success. But it is likely to be a long time before the principle of individual responsibility for rubbish is universally accepted.

Meanwhile, it remains for all those who care about the conservation of our rural environment to seek to promote its welfare in any way we can. If this book has succeeded in outlining some of the ways in which this might be done, albeit in the limited context of hedgerows and verges, it will have achieved one of its principal aims.

172

References

1 Streeter, D. and R. Richardson 1982. *Discovering hedgerows*. London: BBC Books.
2 Wilson, R. 1979. *The hedgerow book*. Newton Abbott: David and Charles.
3 Rule, A. L. 1974. *Hedge building in mid and west Cornwall*. Thesis, School of English, University of Leeds.
4 Pollard, E. 1973. Woodland relic hedges in Huntingdon and Peterborough. *J. Ecol.* **61**, 343–52.
5 Slater, G. 1907. *The English peasantry and the enclosure of the common fields*. London.
6 Davis, G. and J. S. Moore 1979. Agriculture. In *Avon local history handbook*, J. S. Moore (ed.). Chichester: Phillimore.
7 Council for the Protection of Rural England 1971. *Loss of cover through removal of hedgerows and trees*. London: CPRE.
8 Stacey, M. and R. Iles 1983. *Historic landscape survey of the Manor of Englishcombe*. Planning Department, Avon County Council.
9 Bradshaw, A. D. 1971. The significance of hawthorns. In *Hedges and local history*. London: National Council for Social Service.
10 Allen, D. E. 1971. Bramble-dating: promising approach. In *Hedges and local history*. London: National Council for Social Service.
11 Hooper, H. D. 1971. Hedges and history. In *Hedges and local history*. London: National Council for Social Service.
12 Dowdeswell, W. H. 1984. *Ecology. Principles and practice*. London: Heinemann.
13 Willmot, A. 1980. The woody species of hedges with special reference to age in Church Broughton Parish, Derbyshire. *J. Ecol.* **68**, 269–85.
14 Brooks, A. 1980. *Hedging*. Reading: British Trust for Conservation Volunteers.
15 Mitchell, A. F. 1984. *Forestry Commission rule-of-thumb for ageing trees*. Private communication.
16 Polunin, O. 1977. *Trees and bushes of Britain and Europe*. St. Albans: Paladin.
17 Way, J. M. 1972. *Road verges on rural roads. Management and other factors*. Monk's Wood Experimental Station, Natural Environment Research Council.
18 Ranwell, D. S., J. M. Winn and S. E. Allen 1973. *Road salting effects on soil and plants*. Natural Environment Research Council.
19 Scott, N. E. and A. W. Davison 1982. De-icing salt and the invasion of road verges by maritime plants. *Watsonia* **14**, 41–52.

173

20 Dowdeswell, W. H. 1984. *Evolution. A modern synthesis.* London: Heinemann.
21 Pollard, E., M. D. Hooper and N. W. Moore 1979. *Hedges.* London: Collins, New Naturalist.
22 Green, B. 1981. *Countryside conservation.* London: Allen and Unwin.
23 Neal, E. G. 1986. *The natural history of badgers.* Beckenham: Croom Helm.
24 Sheail, J. 1971. *Rabbits and their history.* Newton Abbott: David and Charles.
25 Day, J. C. L. and W. H. Dowdeswell 1968. Natural selection in *Cepaea* on Portland Bill. *Heredity* **23**, 169–88.
26 Eldridge, M. J. 1969. Observations on the food eaten by woodmice (*Apodemus sylvaticus*) and bank voles (*Clethrionomys glareolus*) in a hedge. *J. Zool. Soc. Lond.* **158**, 208–9.
27 Pollard, E. and J. Relton 1970. Hedges V. A study of small mammals in hedges and cultivated fields. *J. Appl. Ecol.* **7**, 549–57.
28 Moore, N. W., M. D. Hooper and B. N. K. Davis 1967. Hedges I. Introduction and reconnaissance studies. *J. Appl. Ecol.* **4**, 201–20.
29 Yapp, W. B. 1961. *Birds and woods.* Oxford: Oxford University Press.
30 Morgan, R. A. and R. J. O'Connor 1980. Farmland habitat and yellowhammer distribution in Britain. *Bird Study* **27**, 155–62.
31 Rands, M. 1983. Partridge breeding populations and hedgerow management. *Game Conservancy Annu. Rev.* **14**, 31–3.
32 Blackwell, J. A. and W. H. Dowdeswell 1950. Local movement in the blue tit. *Br. Birds* **44**, 397–403.
33 Pollard, E. 1968. Hedges IV. A comparison between the Carabidae of a hedge and field site and those of a woodland glade. *J. Appl. Ecol.* **5**, 649–57.
34 Dowdeswell, W. H. 1981. *The life of the meadow brown.* London: Heinemann.
35 Thomas, J. A. 1983. A 'WATCH' census of common butterflies. *J. Biol. Educ.* **17**(4), 333–8.
36 Thomas, J. A. 1983. A quick method for estimating butterfly numbers during surveys. *Biol. Conserv.* **27**, 195–211.
37 Darlington, A. 1968. *Plant galls.* Poole: Blandford Press.
38 Ministry of Transport 1968. *Layout of roads in rural areas.* London: HMSO.
39 Way, J. M. 1976. *Grassed and planted areas of motorways.* Monk's Wood Experimental Station, Natural Environment Research Council.
40 Bradshaw, A. D. and R. D. Roberts 1979. The ecological aspects of establishment on roadside verges. In *The impact of road traffic on plants*, D. M. Colwill (ed.). Transport and Road Research Laboratory.
41 Adams, L. W. and A. D. Geis 1983. Effects of roads on small mammals. *J. Appl. Ecol.* **20**, 403–16.

REFERENCES

42 Braun, S. and W. Flukiger 1984. Increased population of the aphid, *Aphis pomi* at a motorway. Part 1. Field evaluation. *Environ. Pollut.* (*Ser. A*) **33**, 107–20.

43 Port, G. R. and J. R. Thompson 1980. Outbreaks of insect herbivores on plants along motorways in the United Kingdom. *J. Appl. Ecol.* **17**, 649–56.

44 Colwill, D. M. 1979. General environmental effects of motor vehicles. In *The impact of road traffic on plants*, D. M. Colwill (ed.) Transport and Road Research Laboratory.

45 Mansfield, T. A. 1979. The effects of oxides of nitrogen on vegetation. In *The impact of road traffic on plants* D. M. Colwill (ed.). Transport and Road Research Laboratory.

46 Little, P. E. 1979. Deposition of exhaust lead and its impact on plants. In *The impact of road traffic on plants*, D. M. Colwill (ed.) Transport and Road Research Laboratory.

47 Atkins, D. P., I. C. Trueman, C. B. Clarke and A. D. Bradshaw 1982. The evolution of lead tolerance by *Festuca rubra* on a motorway verge. *Environ. Pollut.* (*Ser. A*) **27**, 233–41.

48 Thompson J. R., A. J. Rutter, P. S. Ridout and M. Glover 1979. The implications of the use of de-icing salt for motorway plantings in the UK. In *The impact of road traffic on plants*, D. M. Colwill (ed.). Transport and Road Research Laboratory.

49 Allaby, M. 1970. Where have all the hedges gone? *Ecologist* **1**(4), 8–11.

50 Association of Agriculture 1981. *Hedgerow removal.* London: Association of Agriculture.

51 Elton, C. 1947. *Animal ecology.* London: Sidgwick and Jackson.

52 Sturrock, F. G. and J. Cathie 1980. *Farm modernisation and the countryside.* Department of Land Economy, Cambridge University.

53 Dempster, J. P. 1969. Some effects of weed control on the numbers of the small cabbage white (*Pieris rapae*) on brussels sprouts. *J. Appl. Ecol.* **6**, 339–45.

54 Hooper, H. J. 1976. *The assessment of wind pattern in a pasture field in the lea of a shelter belt of trees by the use of tatter flags.* Private communication.

55 Terrasson, F. and G. Tendron 1981. The case for hedgerows. *Ecologist* **11**(5), 210–20.

56 Bowden, J. and G. W. W. Dean 1977. The distribution of flying insects in and near a tall hedgerow. *J. Appl. Ecol.* **14**, 343–54.

57 Lewis, T. 1969. The distribution of flying insects near a low hedgerow. *J. Appl. Ecol.* **6**, 443–52.

58 Morton, R. K. and N. J. Westwood 1974. Some effects of agricultural change on the English avifauna. *Br. Birds* **67** 41–69.

59 Arnold, G. W. 1983. The influence of ditch and hedgerow structure, length of hedgerows, and area of woodland and garden on bird numbers on farmland. *J. Appl. Ecol.* **20**, 731–50.

60 Van Emden, H. F. and G. F. Williams 1974. Insect stability and diversity in agro-ecosystems. *Annu. Rev. Entomol.* **19**, 455–76.

61 Barker, R. C. 1982. *Managing farm hedges.* Ministry of Agriculture, Fisheries and Food (ADAS) Leaflet 762.
62 Arnold, J. 1968. *The Shell book of country crafts.* London: John Baker.
63 Sherwood, P. T. 1970. *The establishment and maintenance of roadside vegetation. A review of methods available.* Road Research Laboratory, Ministry of Transport.
64 Nature Conservancy Council 1979. *Pesticides.* Nature Conservation Guides Series. Shrewsbury: Nature Conservancy Council.
65 Countryside Commission 1979. *Grass cutting and hedgerow treatment on roadside verges. Code of practice.* Cheltenham: Countryside Commission.
66 Avon Wildlife Trust 1984. Viewpoint. *Avon Wildlife Trust Magazine* **12**, 13.
67 Nature Conservancy Council 1984. *Nature conservation in Britain.* Shrewsbury: Nature Conservancy Council.
68 Rowley, T. and J. Wood 1982. *Deserted villages.* Aylesbury: Shire.
69 Palmer, M. 1981. *Nature conservation and agriculture projects. Hedgerows and walls.* Shrewsbury: Nature Conservancy Council.
70 Nature Conservancy Council 1979. *Hedges and shelterbelts.* Shrewsbury: Nature Conservancy Council.
71 Countryside Commission 1983. *Demonstration farms project: Manor Farm. Farming with conservation.* Cheltenham: Countryside Commission.

Bibliography

Hedgerows and verges – general

Arnold, J. 1968. *The Shell book of country crafts*. London: John Baker. (Describes most country crafts, including the laying of hedges)

Brooks, A. 1980. *Hedging*. Reading: British Trust for Conservation Volunteers. (Excellent work with an emphasis on the practical aspects of hedge planting, maintenance and conservation)

Hoskins, W. G. 1977. *The making of the English landscape*. Harmondsworth: Pelican. (A well known general treatment of the subject)

Pollard, E., M. D. Hooper and N. W. Moore 1979. *Hedges*. London: Collins, New Naturalist. (Excellent authoritative account)

Streeter, D. and R. Richardson 1982. *Discovering hedgerows*. London: BBC Books. (Companion book to a successful television series. Includes country recipes for each month of the year)

Sturrock, F. G. and J. Cathie 1980. *Farm modernisation and the countryside*. Department of Land Economy, Cambridge University. (Modern problems of land management, including hedgerows, seen predominantly from a farming viewpoint)

Thomas, E. and J. T. White 1980. *Hedgerow*. London: Dorling Kindersley. (An elementary approach. Attractively illustrated)

Wilson, R. 1979. *The hedgerow book*. Newton Abbott: David and Charles. (A general account with an emphasis on individual plant and animal species)

Conservation

Beresford, T. 1975. *We plough the fields*. Harmondsworth: Penguin.

Countryside Review Committee 1979. *Conservation and countryside heritage*. London: HMSO.

Dowdeswell, W. H. 1984. *Ecology. Principles and practice*. London: Heinemann.

Fletcher, W. W. 1974. *The pest war*. Oxford: Blackwell.

Green, B. 1981. *Countryside conservation*. London: George Allen and Unwin.

Ratcliffe, D. A. (ed.) 1977. *A nature conservation review*. Cambridge: Cambridge University Press.

Glossary

anaerobic   Lacking oxygen.

Anglo-Saxon Chronicle   A record of Anglo-Saxon history inspired and partly assembled by King Alfred in the late 9th century.

apomixis   The formation of seeds in flowering plants without the need for fertilisation.

assart   An area of cleared woodland let by landowners to tenants for farming from the 12th to 14th centuries.

balks   See **lynchets**.

batology   The study of species of bramble (from the Greek *batos*, bramble).

batter   The slope of a Cornish wall.

bellying   Bulging of the side of a sloping wall.

binders   Lengths of pliable wood such as hazel or willow twisted round the tops of stakes to keep the cut stems of a laid hedge in place. Alternatively known as 'heathers'.

biological control   The control of pests by natural predators or **parasites** rather than by chemical pesticides.

Bronze Age   A period of human history characterised, among other things, by the use of bronze. About 2500 to 550 BC.

calcicole   A plant that thrives on neutral or alkaline soils (see **calcifuge**).

calcifuge   A plant that thrives on lime-free acidic soils (see **calcicole**).

climax   The final stage in an ecological **succession** (sere) under a particular set of ecological conditions.

clone   A group of organisms with the same genetic constitution.

conservation   The control of an ecological environment in a particular state of balance between the various species present involving active management.

detritus   Semi-decomposed organic matter. The term is most commonly used in connection with aquatic habitats (the equivalent of **humus** in soil).

ecological niche   The economic status occupied by an organism within a community, particularly in relation to its food (e.g. herbivore, insectivore, etc.).

ecological succession   See **succession**.

ecology The relationships of living organisms with one another and with the environment.

ecosystem A unit representing the interaction of all the living and non-living components in a particular locality.

enclosures Areas of common land appropriated by landowners for the grazing of livestock. These were surrounded by hedges or fences to prevent animals from straying. The enclosure of land was particularly widespread in the 16th and 19th centuries but occurred at other times as well.

flail A mechanical device for trimming hedges and verges. It is mounted on a tractor and consists of a long adjustable arm carrying a head covered by a metal cowl. Inside it are a number of rotating metal bars that break the stems rather than cutting them.

food chain A diagrammatic representation of the passage of food and other resources through the populations within a community.

food web A way of representing diagrammatically the relationships between a number of different **food chains**.

furlong A group of adjacent strips in a medieval field. The furlong was the basic unit of crop rotation.

galls (plant) Structures on part of a plant (usually the leaf), being a response to the inroad of **parasites** – frequently mites (arachnids) or insects. They are formed either by the multiplication or enlargement of the cells forming the tissues.

halophytes Plants capable of tolerating soils containing a high concentration of salt.

hawthorn The commonest hedgerow shrub. Its name is derived from the Anglo-Saxon for hedge (*hega*).

heathers See **binders**.

hedge The name for a living stockproof barrier surrounding a field. Derived from the Anglo-Saxon word *hecg*.

Herepath (Harepath) An extensive Anglo-Saxon thoroughfare in the Southwest of England running from the Quantocks to Barnstaple. The word means 'army road'.

host A living organism at whose expense a **parasite** exists or on whom another organism lives.

humus Semi-decomposed organic matter in soil.

hydrosere **Succession** beginning with an aquatic community of plants.

indicator species Species of plants that are typical of a particular set of ecological conditions.

intermediate host An organism that houses a stage in the life cycle of a **parasite** other than the adult.

Iron Age A period in human history characterised, among other things, by the use of iron. About 550–50 BC.

lynchets Banks separating medieval strip fields. Also known as 'balks'.

management (of conservation) The process by which **conservation** is achieved. This may include the introduction of external agencies such as the grazing of sheep.

mearestones Large individual stones used to mark the boundaries of property in the 18th century and earlier. They were sometimes inscribed with the names of the landowners concerned.

medieval Referring to the Middle Ages, i.e. 13th to 15th centuries.

open farm A farm that, apart from farming, offers various degrees of public access and other amenities such as the viewing of wildlife.

parasite An organism living partially or completely at the expense of another living animal or plant (the **host**).

pattern A frame, usually made of metal, used in the construction of a field wall in order to ensure the correct slope (**batter**).

Penny Hedge A hedge constructed annually at Whitby, Yorkshire, to commemorate a historical event associated with Whitby Abbey that took place in 1159. Penny is a corruption of 'penance'.

pleachers The partially cut stems of shrubs bent over and used in laying a hedge.

polymorphism The occurrence together of two or more distinct forms of the same species.

quadrat A square of known size. Used as a means of sampling to determine the distribution and density of plants in different localities.

ridge-and-furrow agriculture A pattern of agriculture consisting of strips of land separated by banks (**lynchets**), characteristic of Britain in the Middle Ages.

stakes Lengths of hazel or ash driven into a hedge bank at regular intervals to support a newly laid hedge.

succession (ecological) A series of changes in the plant and animal life of a community from initial colonisation to **climax.**

system An entity comprising a number of interacting parts. The removal or failure of one part may incapacitate the whole system.

territory (breeding) An area established and defended by a pair of animals, usually during the breeding season. In birds it is the locality in which the nest is built.

transect (ecological) A method of measuring and representing graphically the distribution of plants and animals in a particular locality. Belt transects measure horizontal and longitudinal distribution within a band (often one metre wide). Line transects are useful in obtaining a profile of vegetation.

trophic level   The level in a **food web** at which a group of organisms occurs. Green plants (primary producers) are at the lowest level. Tertiary consumers (larger carnivorous animals) are at the highest level.

vector   An animal other than the **host** that acts as a **parasite**'s means of transmission and dispersal.

verge   The strip of vegetation bordering a thoroughfare. It is often divisible into an outer zone of a few centimetres and an inner zone of a metre or more.

Wansdyke   A large bank and ditch traversing many miles of Somerset, Avon and Wiltshire. Its origin is uncertain (Anglo-Saxon or post-Roman) and the western part probably formed the defensive frontier of Somerset.

Wolvesey   The name of Anglo-Saxon origin (meaning 'island of wolves') for part of the city of Winchester. The site of the castle of King Alfred where the **Anglo-Saxon Chronicle** was probably written. Now the name given to the palace of the Bishop of Winchester.

Organisations concerned with hedgerows and verges

Association of Agriculture *Victoria Chambers, 16/20 Stratton Ground, London, SW1P 2HP.* Independent organisation concerned with all aspects of agriculture, including hedgerows

Association for the Protection of Rural Scotland *1 Thistle Court, Edinburgh 2.* The Scottish counterpart of the CPRE in England

Botanical Society of the British Isles *c/o Department of Botany, British Museum (Natural History), Cromwell Road, London, SW7.* Principal botanical society in Britain. Particularly concerned with plant distribution

British Trust for Conservation Volunteers (Headquarters) *10–14 Duke Street, Reading, RG1 4RU.* Organises practical conservation projects and produces publications

British Trust for Ornithology *Beech Grove, Station Road, Tring, Hertfordshire, HP23 5NR.* Research and publications on birds, including hedgerow species

Council for Environmental Education *School of Education, University of Reading, 24 London Road, Reading, RG1 5AQ.* Educational aspects of the environment. Publishes *Directory of Environmental Literature* and *Ecological Teaching Aids*

Council for the Protection of Rural England *4 Hobart Place, London, SW1W 0HY.* Registered charity concerned with the protection and promotion of the beauty of the English landscape. Pressure group on government departments and local authorities

Council for the Protection of Rural Wales *14 Broad Street, Welshpool, Powys, SY21 7SD.* The Welsh counterpart of the CPRE in England

Country Landowners Association *16 Belgrave Square, London, SW1X 8PQ.* Association of private landowners in England and Wales much concerned with conservation aspects

Countryside Commission for England and Wales *John Dower House, Crescent Place, Cheltenham, Gloucestershire, GL50 3RA.* Government organisation responsible for land conservation

Countryside Commission for Scotland *Battleby, Redgorton, Perthshire, PH1 3EW.* Scottish counterpart of the Countryside Commission for England and Wales

Farming and Wildlife Advisory Group *The Lodge, Sandy, Bedfordshire, SG19 2DL.* Advises on all aspects of the relationship between farming and wildlife

ORGANISATIONS CONCERNED WITH HEDGEROWS AND VERGES

Field Studies Council (Headquarters) *9 Devereux Court, Strand, London, WC2R 3JR*. An educational organisation operating numerous field centres and publishing a journal

Forestry Commission *Alice Holt Lodge, Wrecclesham, Farnham, Surrey, GU10 4LN*. Government organisation concerned with forests and their maintenance

Friends of the Earth Trust *377 City Road, London, EC1V 1NA*. Independent action group concerned with environmental conservation

Game Conservancy *Fordingbridge, Hampshire*. Independent organisation concerned with game research and promotion

Institute of Terrestrial Ecology (Publications) *68 Hills Road, Cambridge, CB2 1LA*. Sales of research and other publications of research institutes of the Natural Environment Research Council. Monk's Wood, Abbot's Ripton and Furzebrook Institute,Wareham, particularly, are interested in hedgerow organisms

Mammal Society of the British Isles *Harvest House, 52 London Road, Reading, RG1 5AQ*. The principal British society concerned with all aspects of mammals

Ministry of Agriculture, Fisheries and Food (Publications) *Lion House, Willowburn Estate, Alnwick, Northumberland, NE66 2PF*. Government department responsible for all aspects of food production. Produces many publications including those of the Agricultural Development and Advisory Service (ADAS)

National Association for Environmental Education *18 Barrowdale Close, Exmouth, Devon, EX8 5PN*. Concerned with all aspects of environmental education in schools

Nature Conservancy Council (Interpretive Branch) *Attingham Park, Shrewsbury, SY4 4TW*. Government organisation responsible for the conservation of wildlife in England and Wales

Road Research Laboratory *Crowthorne, Berks*. Controlled by the Department of the Environment (Ministry of Transport). Reviews methods of managing roadside vegetation

Royal Society for Nature Conservation *The Green, Nettleham, Lincoln, LN2 2NR*. National association of Nature Conservation Trusts

Royal Society for the Protection of Birds *The Lodge, Sandy, Bedfordshire, SG19 2DC*. Independent organisation for bird study and conservation

Scottish Landowners Federation *35 Southside Road, Inverness*. The Scottish counterpart of the County Landowners Association in England

Scottish Wildlife Trust *8 Dublin Street, Edinburgh, EH1 3PP*. Scottish counterpart of the Royal Society for Nature Conservation in England

Town and Country Planning Association *17 Carlton House Terrace, London, SW1Y 5AS*. Concerned with all aspects of town and country planning. Numerous publications

Index

Numbers in *italics* indicate pages on which illustrations are included.

187